Victory Over Stroke

STRUCK
BY THE
SILENT
KILLER
Victory Over Stroke

Errol Williams

ISBN 979-8-88757-619-0

Telephone: (305) 735-1041
Email: ncs03@yahoo.com
Website: errolwilliams.maax.site

Cover Design Denis Kaimenyi Guantai

Book Design / Layout D'Edge Media

Edited by Althea Duren / ayebeeduren@gmail.com

Printed in the U.S.A

Dedication

My great wife Angela deserves my gratitude for her generosity, love, and tolerance throughout what must have been a very trying time for her. No matter how many people's lives my book affects, know that you contributed to its success. I love and thank you, "Babes."

To Niketa and Christian Jerome, our two wonderful kids. I naturally value your unwavering affection. Our two grandsons, Nathan and Jeremiah, as well as Jonathan, our son-in-law, truly love you guys.

To my church family, New Alpha Worship Center, as your pastor and a fellow worker in God's Kingdom, I am touched and grateful for the generosity shown to me by you all. I am really appreciative.

To Pastor Hilma Tucker, "Let's Go Buddy." If you had not taken my blood pressure, things might have turned out differently. I am forever grateful; thank you.

To my talented Kenyan brother, Denis Kaimenyi Guantai. You served as my graphic designer. Thanks for your insight and gracious support.

Acknowledgements

No man ever succeeds without the collective effort of numerous others who have his best interests in mind, individuals who are devoted and willing to do whatever it takes to see them succeed. Therefore, this book is the result of innumerable individuals whose inspirations, suggestions, and "push" made it possible.

Preface

The book you are holding may be the most significant reality check on your health that you have experienced recently. I can say this with certainty, not because I wrote it, but rather because the topic is most urgent.

Over the years, I have attempted to write on a wide range of themes, but I have never felt compelled to do so, nor have I ever had the self-control necessary to finish any of them. However, when I was diagnosed with high blood pressure, also referred to as hypertension and the "Silent Killer," I was in grave risk of dying, and I believe the Holy Spirit wants me to share this experience with anybody who will read, share, and pay attention. It has never been more crucial for me to be aware of my health and the value of treating my body as God's temple.

Even though I have an unfathomable amount of desire to treat my body well, one of my biggest challenges is having the "discipline" to carry out that goal. This may be true for others as well.

I do, however, think that if we, especially those who are in positions of leadership of God's people, cannot set an example by leading a disciplined life with regard to our health, then we may be acting hypocritically by telling others that Jesus Christ is calling them to live a disciplined life. "Let your light so shine before men, that they may see your good works, and glorify your Father which is in heaven" (Matthew 5:16).

Should Christians who are aware of "the truth" suffer from the same health problems as people who are not saved including food-related illnesses such as high blood pressure, diabetes, and high cholesterol? "And ye shall know the truth, and the truth shall make you free" (John 8:32).

God said, "My people are destroyed for lack of knowledge: because thou hast rejected knowledge, I will also reject thee" (Hosea 4:6). Knowledge is available. The word of God tells me that my body is "the temple of God." "What? know ye not that your body is the temple of the Holy Ghost which is in you, which ye have of God, and ye are not your own?" (1 Corinthians 6:19).

Satan is to blame for many evil deeds, but I am also accountable for what I eat, how much I consume, and how long I consume it. My biggest hope is that this book may at the very least prompt you to examine how you are treating God's temple in order to avoid being victimized by the "Silent Killer." I appreciate your kind support.

Errol E. Williams

Forward

From esteemed educators, preeminent politicians, and bodacious billion-aires to acclaimed athletes, memorable musicians, and world-class writers, it is evident that over the course of my life I have been able to shake hands with prominent people who have majorly impacted the world. Despite the greatness of all of the notable individuals I have been able to come across, I am most grateful for the day I met the laudable leader, passionate pastor, and faithful follower of Jesus Christ that Apostle Errol Williams embodies. His zeal for God, the things of God, and the advancement of God's people serves as the fuel he uses to push individuals like myself from places of paltry living to purposeful reigning.

Having him as a spiritual father for the last 10 years, I have not just been a sheep of the congregation he shepherds; on the contrary, I'm a member of a family with a selfless head of household who, like John the Baptist, clears the path for those under his leadership to step into what God has called them to do. For this reason, I am no longer the oafish, oblivious eight-year-old who he baptized that lacked true understanding of who God had called me to be. I stand as an eighteen-year-old award-winning writer and speech artist who leads an award-winning Christian youth organization that has evangelized, educated, and cultivated over 200 teenagers so far to be effective in the body of Christ.

This testimony of my transformation and the similar personal experiences that countless others can recall for themselves would have been impossible without the transformative power of Apostle Errol Williams' leadership. He is a world changer. Once you meet him and begin to partake of the ministry God has called him to, you will never be the same.

I recall sitting in the pew during praise and worship of our routine Sunday services. As always, Apostle Williams had his hands on the keyboard, serving as a minstrel unto the Lord, stretching out the strings to set the atmosphere in the sanctuary, monitoring the room as the set man of the house, listening to God's next instruction, but then, boom. That was the sound of his body hitting the ground as he passed out behind the keyboard. Shrieks filled members of the church as his daughter, Niketa, ran out the room frantically with tears in her red eyes and a cell phone at her ear to call 911.

Years later, I was sitting at a lunch table at my high school when I received the regretful phone call from my mother that informed me that the pastor who changed my life was just admitted into the hospital because he had a stroke. I instantly recalled my grandmother who was left a paralytic after having a stroke years prior. I grew fearful but still kept the faith in the healing power of God that Apostle Williams constantly taught about.

Within this book, it will be the fervor for God's people and desire for vengeance on the "Silent Killer" that Apostle Errol Williams will use as ammunition to shoot down the unhealthy customs God's people allow to perpetuate in their lives. As he takes you through the journey of his personal experiences, you will be challenged in the area of your health to ensure your overall spiritual, emotional, and physical wealth and wellbeing. You are no longer just a reader, but you have just been adopted into the family of believers that he fathers to ensure they grow into mature believers. This comes with love and support, but also the beatings of correction. In the words of scripture "For the moment all discipline seems painful rather than pleasant, but later it yields the peaceful fruit of righteousness to those who have been trained by it" (English Standard Version; Hebrews 12:1). I believe this book will produce fruit in you as you dig into each page.

Ayeisha Kirkland ("The Young Evangelist")

Contents

CHAPTER 1
Why Did I Get Sick?

I do not think God gave man the potential to be sick, even if I will never be able to pinpoint the exact cause of my illness. God undoubtedly wanted humans to have eternal life through Adam and Eve. "Wherefore, as by one man sin entered into the world, and death by sin; and so death passed upon all men, for that all have sinned" (Romans 5:12). God never intended death! Death in all its forms is a contradiction of God's creation, and a result of sin!

Adam's action brought about sin and its consequences for humanity because there was no sin, disease, or death prior to his deed. It is obvious that natural evil is a result of moral evil; if man had never sinned, he would not have experienced its consequences. The text of Genesis 3:19, "For dust thou art, and unto dust shalt thou return," was not spoken until after Adam had consumed the forbidden fruit. And so, both physical and spiritual death entered into this world through Adam's original sin.

Man was warned by God with death as a penalty for disobedience. So death as punishment for man's disobedience was a judicial part of the fallen creation, not a natural part of God's original plan for man. "But of the tree of the knowledge of good and evil, thou shalt not eat of it: for in the day that thou eatest thereof thou shalt surely die" (Genesis 2:17).

Paul puts it this way in Romans 6:23, "For the wages of sin is death; but the gift of God is eternal life through Jesus Christ our Lord." Before the flood, some of our predecessors lived ten times longer than we do now. For instance, Jared, the father of Enoch, lived to the age of 962 while Adam lived for 930 years.

Struck By The Silent Killer

Methuselah lived the longest life ever, clocking in at 969 years. He was Noah's grandfather and the son of Enoch, the only person to have never died when God took him at the age of 365. However, the average human life expectancy dramatically decreased after the flood.

After the deluge, the earth looked nothing like it did previously. I believe there was no sickness because it would have taken some time for sickness and disease to grow and intensify after Adam and Eve had fallen from their original state of perfection.

Their extended life cannot be attributed just to the fact that the food they ate pre-flood was far superior in terms of extending their years on the earth. I believe long life spans were a necessity in the beginning if the earth was to be filled by people (Genesis 1:26). Otherwise, fulfilling the commandment to populate the earth would have taken an inordinate amount of time. "And God blessed them, and God said unto them, 'Be fruitful, multiply, and replenish the earth'" (Genesis 1:28).

Because the planet's first occupants lived for such a long time, they would have progressed in all aspects of life, including an understanding of the necessary foods which would have helped them live longer. Other elements, such as the environment, absence of radiation, water purity, and air quality, could have contributed to their longevity. What is undeniable is that man's purposeful disobedience to God's command tainted God's original plan for him to live eternally free from everything that followed.

Although the Bible does not specify what the pre-flood diet consisted of, I believe Adam and his ancestors followed the nutritional pattern that God gave him in Genesis 1:29, "And God said, 'Behold, I have given you every herb bearing seed, which is upon the face of all the earth, and every tree, in which is the fruit of a tree yielding seed; to you it shall be for meat.'" This verse leads me to believe that before the flood, the people were vegetarians. Many people who believe in the advantages of their favored diet will undoubtedly disagree with this assertion. However, it is difficult to deny that man's ancestral diet was significantly superior to that of modern man. It is also indisputable that our present eating habits are killing us and silly to argue that diet has no significant role in people's health and longevity.

Following the flood, people's lifespans decreased precipitously. Noah lived 350 years after the flood and died at the age of 950. But why did everyone have a shorter life span after the flood? Was it just because of changes in their diet or climatic condition?

The solution has to do with man's conduct in God's view. According to Genesis 6:2, God was dissatisfied with man's behavior, therefore he determined the length of humanity's lifespan. "Yet his days shall be an hundred and twenty years" (Genesis 6:3). God decided that 120 years was to be the maximum lifespan of humanity. However, a number of Israel patriarchs lived longer than this. Abraham, for example, lived to be 175 years old (Genesis 25:7) and Isaac lived to be 180 years old (Genesis 35:28). Also, according to Deuteronomy 34:7, Moses lived to be 120 years old and had perfect vision. "And Moses was an hundred and twenty years old when he died: his eye was not dim, nor his natural force abated." Moses' good health, I believe, was bestowed on him so that he might complete his mission.
There is no attempt in the Bible to deny the existence of sickness. In reality, from the beginning to the end of the Bible, we encounter the realities of sickness, dying, and death. It is something we will all have to deal with for the rest of our lives on this sinful planet. But why do some people get sick while others do not? It is a conundrum that no one can answer with any certainty.

There are many who assume that germs and genes cause diseases and sickness. If germs and disease are the causes of sickness, both affect us all. It is true that germs may cause many different varieties of sickness in people. These can vary in seriousness from mild to extremely serious or deadly. However, God gave man a nutritious diet so that he might achieve and retain perfect health and prevent the development of chronic diseases at all stages of his life.

Growing old was once considered a huge consideration or a major factor for causing illness. Aging is now known not to be a direct cost. Being healthy into one's 80s is the expectation but if neglected in old age, the body becomes more susceptible to disease.

Despite the fact that our diet is killing us, my ambition is to live to be a hundred and twenty years old.

Struck By The Silent Killer

Some may snicker and laugh, but Terah, the father of Abram was "two hundred and five years" at death (Genesis 11:32). The Bible is replete with examples of individuals that lived a long life on the earth. "And these are the days of the years of Abraham's life which he lived, an hundred threescore and fifteen years [175 years]" (Genesis 25:7). "But Jehoiada waxed old, and was full of days when he died; an hundred and thirty years old was he when he died" (2 Chronicles 24:15).

My illness could have been brought on by both physical and spiritual factors. It is simple to say, "Satan did this to me," which is only true in the sense that he is the source of all disease, death, and sickness. But did I contribute in any way, and was I abiding by God's food laws?

It is critical that we comprehend this crucial fact. If you breach any of God's laws, you can expect him to punish you appropriately. Adam held his wife responsible for his sin against God. It is all too easy to point the finger at others for our bad behavior. However, it was shown by scripture that it was the result of Adam and Eve's initial sin. Sickness is something that we will all have to cope with in this fallen world we live in, and it will be with us for as long as we are in these bodies.

Indeed, there are times when people get sick simply because they violate the laws which God has established. In other words, if we do not adhere to divine laws, we leave ourselves open to the devil. In Exodus 15:26, God gave a solemn warning, "And said, If thou wilt diligently hearken to the voice of the LORD thy God, and wilt do that which is right in his sight, and wilt give ear to his commandments, and keep all his statutes, I will put none of these diseases upon thee, which I have brought upon the Egyptians: for I am the LORD that healeth thee." Their adherence to the Lord's voice was the foundation of their long life free from disease. What if they decided not to comply? Then, by default, they would be saying, "We want all of those diseases."

The hazards of eating particular foods are frequently discussed by medical professionals. Many spend a lot of their hard-earned money on doctors to advise them on what is and is not healthy for their bodies, but since they have free will and poor self-control, they choose to do the opposite and then wonder why their health does not improve.

Adam and Eve were told that the death process would begin if they disobeyed God, "...for in the day that thou eatest thereof thou shalt surely die" (Genesis 2:17). Sickness is part of that "surely die" process. Sadly, they did willfully break God's command and ate of the forbidden fruit. Since then, humanity has had to deal with death and dying.

Sickness can also be the result of sin. While sickness is not sin, it is possible for sickness to be the result of sin. Paul emphasized that our body is the temple of the Holy Spirit. He wrote the following to the Corinthians. "What? Know ye not that your body is the temple of the Holy Ghost which is in you, which ye have of God, and ye are not your own?" (1 Corinthians 6:19). Knowing that our bodies are God's temples but consciously defiling them by utilizing them as garbage disposals is a sin against God.

Sometimes sickness results for a very simple reason – people do not take care of themselves; they overindulge in food, alcohol, or work. They let their body run down to the place where it is susceptible to illness. I did not eat too much or drink too much, but I did not pay enough attention to what my body needed for nutrition or what I had eaten, which was immoral of me and may have led to the stroke. Since then, I have apologized for my transgressions and made a commitment not to eat anything that contains sin.

The Scripture teaches that sickness can actually result from overwork in God's ministry. In fact, Paul wrote that a fellow Christian worker, Epaphroditus, was sick to the point of death because of his work for the Lord. We read the following words to the Philippians, "Because for the work of Christ he was nigh unto death, not regarding his life, to supply your lack of service toward me" (Philippians 2:30).

Well-intentioned men and women have been ill and even perished while laboring for the Lord, oblivious to the fact that they were breaking God's laws. Ignorance is never a good thing. James, the author, warns us about this. "If any of you lack wisdom, let him ask of God, that giveth to all men liberally, and upbraideth not; and it shall be given him" (James 1:5). In Hosea 4:6, Hosea expressed similar feelings when he said, "My people are destroyed for lack of knowledge."

Struck By The Silent Killer

Lack of rest might also play a role in getting sick. We see Jesus leading by example when he tells his disciples to take a break from their ministry work. Mark jots down the following story. "And he said unto them, 'Come ye yourselves apart into a desert place, and rest a while': for there were many coming and going, and they had no leisure so much as to eat" (Mark 6:31). I frequently lacked discipline when it came to taking breaks for food and relaxation. The "coming and going" of the many had become my obsession. It is one of the causes of the high death rate in today's church society. Some people pass away prematurely, while others experience church "burnout."

People can get sick if they do not get enough exercise, just as they can if they don't get enough sleep. On both counts, I am to blame. I would never consider myself a slacker, but I could have done a lot better with both. If we do not exercise or rest our bodies, we will be subjected to a variety of illnesses and diseases, as well as mortality. In addition, as we study the Old Testament Scripture, we find that the Lord provided the means where the people would get sufficient exercise as well as sufficient rest. One day out of seven, one week out of seven, one month out of seven, and one year out of seven, the people took a break from their job. Rest, like physical labor, was an important component of their life. As a result, God permits for both exercise and repose.

Sickness is not a sin in and of itself. However, there were ailments sent to people as a result of their wrongdoing. The following episode is recounted.

Moses' only family members were jealous of his newfound power and decided to launch a revolt against his leadership. "And Miriam and Aaron spake against Moses because of the Ethiopian woman whom he had married: for he had married an Ethiopian woman" (Numbers 12:1). Despite the religious obligations of Miriam as a prophetess and Aaron as a priest, they conspired against Moses, God's chosen man, and Miriam contracted leprosy as a result. Many people are unwell, in my opinion, because they have spoken negatively against God's workers.

The moral of the story is that if you are in a position of leadership, you should expect criticism, even from family members, but if you leave it to God, he will make the appropriate judgment.

"Miriam became leprous, white as snow: and Aaron looked upon Miriam, and, behold, she was leprous" (Numbers 12:10). The authority of God's chosen leader must be respected; to rebel against such a leader is to rebel against God himself. Miriam would have died if Aaron had not pleaded with Moses on their behalf. "And Aaron said unto Moses, 'Alas, my lord, I beseech thee, lay not the sin upon us, wherein we have done foolishly, and wherein we have sinned'" (Numbers 12:11).

As written in the Bible, "Now the man Moses was very meek, above all the men which were upon the face of the earth" (Numbers 12:3). Could it be that his brother and sister mistook his meekness for weakness since he was a meek man?

He could have rejoiced in God's just punishment, which he did not pray for, but we see him instead acting as an Intercessor on their behalf. "And Moses cried unto the LORD, saying, 'Heal her now, O God, I beseech thee'" (Numbers 12:13). Her sentence was reduced from death to a seven-day expulsion from the camp, thanks to his prayers. And when all was done, he reinstated them to full position.

If you are in a position of power, realize that not everyone will be happy for you; you will likely face opposition, just as Moses did. Yet, if your authority comes from God, those who oppose are opposing God, and He will battle on your behalf if you allow Him to do so. Even if people who oppose you become ill, pray for their healing, and do not carry grudges against them.

God's people, for the most part, are not always grateful, and He does not always get the praise He deserves. The Lord struck down the evil king Herod Agrippa for not giving glory to the Lord. The Book of Acts records what happened in this manner. "And immediately the angel of the Lord smote him, because he gave not God the glory: and he was eaten of worms, and gave up the ghost" (Acts 12:23). We find that the Lord, at times, uses sickness, disease, and death as a means of judgment. The judgment for this godless king was death. This was God's righteous judgment for his sin of ingratitude.

Struck By The Silent Killer

There are instances where sickness can originate with the devil. We find this from a statement from Jesus when He healed an infirmed woman. "And, behold, there was a woman which had a spirit of infirmity eighteen years, and was bowed together, and could in no wise lift up herself. And when Jesus saw her, he called her to him, and said unto her, 'Woman, thou art loosed from thine infirmity'" (Luke 13:12).

The origins of disease, physical abnormalities, and paralysis are frequently the subject of theological arguments. This lesson clearly demonstrates that Satan was directly responsible for this woman's paralysis. "And ought not this woman, being a daughter of Abraham, whom Satan hath bound, lo, these eighteen years, be loosed from this bond on the sabbath day?" (Luke 13:16).

While on earth, Jesus' adversaries were not only individuals, like as the hypocrites in this lesson, but also Satan himself. Practitioners of the gospel of Jesus would be well to learn from this that while some illnesses are caused only by natural causes, others are directly linked to spirits, and they are demonically influenced.

Whatever the cause of the illness, all can be set free via the words of Jesus Christ, including from stroke paralysis. "And when Jesus saw her, he called her to him, and said unto her, Woman, thou art loosed from thine infirmity" (Luke 13:12). As the writer of Psalms 107:20 reminds us, the word of Jesus has healing power, "He sent his word, and healed them, and delivered them from their destructions."

We should not assume that sickness is always negative. There can be positive benefits derived from sickness. The Lord can use sickness to discipline us and cause us to change our habits and thus follow Him more closely. The psalmist wrote, "Before I was afflicted I went astray: but now have I kept thy word" (Psalms 119:67). Scripture speaks of both physical and spiritual causes for sickness. This being the case, we should not always complain when we suffer. Instead, we should look for something positive to come out of it.

Both physical and spiritual causes could have contributed to my condition. Saying "Satan caused this to me" seems straightforward, but that is only accurate in the sense that he is the root of all illness, death, and disease. However, did I make any contributions, and did I abide by God's dietary and other laws?

The scripture reads, "It is good for me that I have been afflicted; that I might learn thy statutes" (Psalms 119:71). It is critical that we comprehend this crucial fact. If you breach any of God's laws, you can expect Him to punish you appropriately. Adam held his wife responsible for his sin against God. It is all too easy to point the finger at others for our bad behavior. There can be actual benefits from suffering. Let us learn them well. "My people are destroyed for lack of knowledge" (Hosea 4:6).

In sum, there are a number of reasons as to why people get sick. Therefore, we cannot assume that each time a person is sick there is only one cause for their sickness. Indeed, there are many possibilities as to why I was struck by the "Silent Killer," clinically termed hypertension and commonly known as high blood pressure.

CHAPTER 2
As a Pastor

"P astor" is near the bottom of the list of respectable professions as servants of God; formerly, they were just slightly above "car salesperson." Pastors, like Jesus, are first and foremost "servants" tasked with shepherding God's flock. "For even the Son of Man did not come to be ministered unto, but to minister, and to give his life a ransom for many" (Mark 10:45). Despite the fact that Jesus was sent to be a servant and did not come to be ministered to, the angels of God tended to him when he vanquished Satan in the wilderness of his temptations. "Then the devil leaveth him, and, behold, angels came and ministered unto him" (Matthew 4:11).

The pastor's responsibility is to prepare God's church for ministry. I obviously did not perform that well. I considered it my duty to serve every ministry. According to theology, the shepherd is responsible for the overall care of any ministry, but not for doing everything in the ministry. I took my job and responsibilities as the pastor very seriously, and I understood that if I abdicated my role, I would have to account to God. However, I was not constantly aware of my own limitations.

The hymn of "delegation" is a popular church anthem and recommendation. However, finding enough saved people who are willing to "roll up their sleeves" and perform Kingdom work in my opinion is one of the hardest things for many pastors. Because most rescued people are unaware of their place in the body, pastors have it particularly difficult. However, in 1 Corinthians 12:1, Paul said, "Now concerning spiritual gifts, brethren, I would not have you ignorant."

Struck By The Silent Killer

It is a truth that most "brethren" are unaware of their roles or responsibilities inside the church. As a result, it is up to the pastor to do both their tasks and his own. If there are not any other people nearby who are willing and able to do it, should the pastor forego chores like cleaning the bathrooms and putting out the trash?

He is not seen as someone who will become sick like the rest of us. However, if the exact nature of the pastor's work were known, it would be clear that what is a possibility for many is a probability for him.

Even if he is not working at a hospital as a doctor or other medical specialist, the pastor, like Jesus, is continually exposed to spiritual and physical ailments. He is expected to visit those members of his flock who are afflicted with various illnesses on a regular basis. He may not even be aware that his immune system is weakened when he believes he has caught "just a cold." This could go unnoticed for a while, as "just a cold" is not a sign that he should downsize or reduce his workload.

As a pastor, I am not one to admit to being overworked. Although I was always aware of the danger of being unwell, I would never have entertained the concept of being struck by the "Silent Killer," having a stroke, or becoming a stroke statistic.

"As a man of God, I believe in a God who heals all sort of sickness and diseases, and if I should fall sick, what can God not heal?" That is what I would say to myself. Is it possible that I was not acting in accordance with God's will? In Hosea 4:6, God says, "My people are destroyed because of a lack of knowledge."

Moses was the leader of a group of enraged, rebellious, and bloodthirsty Israelites. Dealing with them proved to be a major challenge for Moses. This just goes to prove that even the best of vessels can be flawed.

"And when Moses' father-in-law saw all that he did to the people, he said, 'What is this thing that thou doest to the people? Why sittest thou thyself alone, and all the people stand by thee from morning unto even?'" (Exodus 18:14). According to the narrator, the people came to Moses with their concerns from morning to evening, much like people have come to me with their troubles from time to time.

Jethro detected a possible "burnout" candidate, as well as zeal without expertise. Moses had a policy of welcoming all people. Despite the fact that he was anointed and referred to as a prophet of God and what he was doing was beneficial to the people and in line with God's will, it was harmful to his health. His father-in-law noticed that not only what he was doing was taking up too much of his time, but he had also overburdened himself with irrelevant activities. Yes, he was in command of the masses, but he needed to delegate some responsibilities to others.

I am aware of moments when I had become overly preoccupied with minor details. I did not have enough time to do the essentials. It was up to me to figure out what the most important things were and prioritize them. Instead, I would allow myself to focus on minor matters, but as essential as they may be, they would deplete my energy and power for the more vital tasks. Even though I did not practice or study the advice given to Moses by his father-in-law, Jethro, this should serve as a lesson to all pastors.

The devil must get a kick out of suffocating people with trivialities. "Pastor, can you kindly drive me to 'the store,' 'the mall,' or wherever?" I remember getting that type of call when I wanted to spend time in the word and prayer. I would find myself "waiting on tables" a lot. Not that these requests are beneath me as a "servant," and I would gladly fulfill them, but in the grand scheme of things, they take time away from Bible study and prayer.

The caution of Moses' father-in-law had no influence on Moses' authority or position as God's appointed ruler over his people. Instead, he showed him how to outsource countless jobs to others in order to be more productive, save energy, and focus on more important concerns. "What you're doing isn't good," he told Moses. Jethro served as a mentor or coach to Moses, giving him explicit instructions on what to do and how to do it. While some people will recognize the issue, they will be unable to provide a solution.

Struck By The Silent Killer

I do not believe many pastors have friends or mentors who have demonstrated a deep grasp of the value of self-care in practice or theory for whatever reason. I believe that this aspect of life has proven to be a serious concern for pastors, including myself.

What would have happened to Moses if Jethro had not been such a wise mentor? Could he have had a stroke from the stress of ministry or have burned out much sooner? Few people fully comprehend the pressures that a pastor faces on a daily basis. It goes beyond the stressful process of spending many hours studying and praying in preparation for Sunday sermons. In addition to studying for Bible study, he has the work of presenting that message in an appropriate manner, and then he has to plan to do it all over again after descending from the pulpit, even if no one shows up on Sunday.

He has to deal with life out of the pulpit for himself and others, save or unsaved. He cannot refuse a bill from the mail man because he is a pastor. Often times he has the added burden of thinking about the bills of his flock. In addition, pastors must sometimes put out fires among brethren who fail to obey scriptural mandates on how to squash indifferences among themselves, as well as reach out to individuals who are backsliding and immature believers.

All of these are serious responsibilities for the pastor that cannot be passed on to uncaring others when they are of no real concern to them. A true pastor always has his people's best interests at heart. He keeps them in his heart even when he goes on vacation. Others may not understand this conduct because they are not called to this degree of ministry, but precautionary measures must be taken to avoid self-destruction.

Regardless, many people have struggled to understand their fast-deteriorating health of which they are aware of or unaware. Because there is no audible warning, a condition like the **"Silent Killer"** may go unnoticed for years in the life of a pastor or anybody else.

It is not unusual for pastors to work between 55 and 75 hours a week. The assertion is that they frequently are unable to spend the essential amount of time with their families because of their church duties.

Preparation for a single-hour-long sermon can take up to fifteen hours, which is a significant amount of time. These lengthy hours must take a toll on his health, as well as the health of his family and that of the church as a whole.

Although I am confident that God desires every church and pastor to be healthy and profitable, there is a sense of malaise and misunderstanding about what constitutes a healthy church and pastor. Health encompasses not just bodily well-being but also spiritual, emotional, occupational, and financial well-being. To be regarded entirely healthy, a pastor must address all parts of his life.

Many pastors lack real connections; they may be connected to a large number of people, but building genuine friendships is extremely difficult for them because their local group consists of the people they are shepherding. And despite the fact that pastors face some of the same challenges as the people they serve, they are rarely thought of as "just like everyone else." Pastors, in particular, do not seek counseling, despite their hard workload. They feel the agony when one of their sheep struggles, goes astray, falls, or abandons the faith while no one else notices. Throughout their ministry days, they are confronted with a wide range of challenges, including bereavement, loss, suicide, illness, disease, and despair, to name a few. They are supposed to deal with other people's emotions and still be a rock of strength for them. Thank God for the Jethro spirit mentors who can see and hear pastors are crying out, "I need support. I am in need. Help me." even if this cry is not articulated.

I believe the stress of looking after the flock has risen, especially since the release of COVID-19 in 2020. The outbreak has probably had wide range of effects on the church and especially the health of pastors. I speculate that many are considering leaving the ministry. Some may be leaving because of exhaustion and stress, but I suppose the main reason pastors leave is because the people they serve do not always follow the pastor's lead and share the same goals. Even if the pastor feels that God is leading him in a particular direction, if his congregation refuses to adhere to or follow this behavior, it may stress the pastor out more than anything else.

CHAPTER 3
The Morning It "Struck"

O n the morning the **"Silent Killer"** struck me, irreversibly changing my life, there were no obvious signals of impending danger. It was the day after I had led a healing service at church, which included recorded testimony of persons who had received divine healing

I have always thought, and continue to think, that it is God's will for us to be healthy on all levels. The Bible is replete with His desire for His people to be healthy at all times. Moses reiterated God's desire of this for His extremely special people early in the deliverance of the children of Israel from Egyptian slavery. While God desired complete and total healing for them, it was still based on their unwavering devotion to His word. "And you shall worship the LORD your God, and he shall bless thy bread and thy water, and I will remove illness from among you" (Exodus 23:25).

I had just finished my breakfast the morning of the stroke, which was not my regular routine. I have never been a great fan of breakfast. When I got up from the table, my left leg felt odd and heavy. I did not think much of it, despite the fact that I had never felt that way before. My capacity to move quickly had not been hampered in the past.

This time the short trek to the kitchen, where I deposited the breakfast dish, was a struggle for me. While my tablet was in my left hand, my grip on the device slipped. "What caused it to fall?"

Struck By The Silent Killer

I had always been careful how I carried it, and I had always kept a solid grasp on it. I did not put in further thought into why it dropped.

I went and lied down for a few minutes to give my leg time to fix itself, or so I thought. I was not agitated during this event, anxious but not overly concerned, perhaps since there was no pain or other discomfort other than my leg feeling heavy. During this time of reflection, my mind was now being besieged with a cascade of mixed thoughts, the chief of which was, "Is this a retaliatory act of Satan? Is this one of his ways of getting back at me because of the successful healing service we had the day before?"

At that point, the Holy Spirit reminded me of two scriptural verses. The first was 1 Thessalonians 5:18, "In everything give thanks: for this is the will of God in Christ Jesus concerning you," and Romans 8:2, "And we know that all things work together for good to them that love God, to them who are the called according to his purpose."

With a burst of faith and expectancy, I thanked God for my healing while inspecting my leg, hoping that it had totally recovered so I could get on with the plans I had for the morning and my radio program that was scheduled for that evening. Despite the lack of visible change, an immense sense of serenity washed over me as I thanked and blessed God.

But not long after I had concluded my thanksgiving and felt satisfied, I began to consider what else I could do. I remember begging Angela, my wife, to pray for me and anoint the leg with oil. When she finished praying, I decided to elevate my leg, but my condition did not seem to change as a result of this action.

Satan spoke to my mind. He taunted me. His voice was loud and menacing. I remember him saying, "So you're telling others about this God who is a Healer? Where's He now? You have prayed and are you healed? Will you continue to talk about this God who can heal people?" These and many other thoughts bombarded my mind.

After that, I examined Satan's words and thought, "Can I tell the church family that God is still a healer? Will I have any credibility among the people? Is my lack of faith why I am not instantaneously healed? " These thoughts, and a jillion more, were on parade in my head.

I subsequently made the decision that if I was not better by the morning, I was going to spend the next three days at the church in prayer and fasting based on what Jesus told his disciples in Matthew 17: 21: "Howbeit this kind goeth not out but by prayer and fasting," the call for urgent prayer. Meanwhile, I remembered a section in the book of James when the author inquired, "Is there any sick among you?" It was and still is common to find the bodies of saints and unsaved people suffering from an array of ailments and illnesses, some of which are fatal. James further instructed them on what to do. "Let them call for the elders of the church; and let them pray over him, anointing him with oil in the name of the Lord. And the prayer of faith shall save the sick, and the Lord shall raise him up; and if he has committed sins, they shall be forgiven
him" (James 5:14-15).

With the exception of the occasional cold or flu, I had never been afflict-ed by illness. I felt healthy and nimble, despite the fact that I had never thought of myself as the embodiment of perfect health. I recall having suf-fered short-term chest pain from time to time. I have no way of know-ing for sure if these ailments had anything to do with what happened to me. I suppose I will never know. However, these episodes were never long enough to disrupt my normal daily routine nor to cause me anxiety.

At this point, I was torn between two options. First, I heard a voice in my head say, "Call for the elders of the church." It is impossible for me to de-scribe how the voice sounded in words. It was not particularly loud or noisy; rather, it was more of an intuitive whisper. If I were to pick a favorite verse, 1Thessalonians 5:18 would be right at the top of them. I would quite literally find myself audibly reciting this verse aloud, "In everything, give thanks, for this is the will of God in Christ Jesus concerning you," and also Psalms 18:6, "In my distress I called upon the LORD, and cried in my God: he heard my voice out of his temple, and my cry came before him, even into his ears." Then, an opposing voice remarked hastily, "But you are the pastor. They are supposed to call you. You're not the one who's supposed to contact them." For a little period, I agreed with that voice. I occupied myself for a while by looking up scriptural reasons of why I, the pastor, should not call. Because it seemed so innocent at the time, I did not realize it was the ene-my speaking to me.

Struck By The Silent Killer

I know God speaks to his children, but I also know Satan speaks to God's people in order to fool them into not obtaining what is rightfully theirs. I have been duped by the adversary over the years because I have not always brought "every thought captive," as stated in 2 Corinthians 10:5. Every decision we make requires the ability to clearly hear God's voice. Making a poor decision based on the voice of the enemy can result in disaster.

It is common knowledge that what a person believes has an impact on how they act. King Solomon declares, "For as he thinketh in his heart, so is he" (Proverbs 7:23). Our minds are the heart of our emotions. God is calling us to adjust our ways of behaving in a way that honors His name. So, rather than focusing on outer behavior, what we present to the world, we should focus on disciplining the mind, which is the source of our thoughts and actions.

I heard a much louder but inaudible and unexplained voice repeat the word "pride" as I agreed with the enemy that the people should call me. I was taken aback. I think I said "pride" more than once. But, I thought, "I'm not a proud person." "Then do what God's Word says," came the retort.

The spirit of pride has kept many individuals from receiving deliverance because they either do not know how to recognize God's voice or they actively choose to heed the devil's voice, allowing the enemy to triumph over them. I was on the verge of succumbing to that vengeful spirit.

Calling for the Elders
Even after all of that, summoning the elders was a difficult task. My pulse was racing when I finally grabbed my phone and dialed our church's emergency number to send in an urgent prayer request. I gave a quick rundown of my symptoms and referred to the section of James that explains what sick people should do. I requested that the elders call my wife to arrange a time for them to come and pray for me.

In retrospect, I made a scriptural misstep by asking the elders to establish a time to come and pray for me. The sick should call the presbyters or pastors of the church, according to James. Was asking my wife to schedule a time in accordance with scripture's directive?

Victory Over Stroke

The importance of adhering to a clear scriptural mandate cannot be over-stated. The order in which James provides the directive is critical, and I realized then that I definitely did not follow the scripture's requirements. To some, this may seem like a minor thing, but I disagree; God is a God of order, and I believe He wants us to follow His rules. It was simple to identify the sick because they would be the ones to call. In my case, I was sick; therefore, culpability was on me to call for the elders of the church.

We sometimes wonder why the sick among us are not healed. While I don't have any clear answers, I am convinced that God will keep His promises as mentioned in Numbers 23:19: "God is not a man, that he should lie; neither the son of man, that he should repent: hath he said, and shall he not do it? or hath he said spoken, and shall he not make it good?"

Even though God gives this admonition to His people, calling for the elders it is not a behavior that is commonly practiced. Many sick people in church do not always call for the elders. For whatever reason, they prefer to contact a friend or physician before contacting the elders. Is it any wonder that very often the desired result for healing is not achieved?

I feel that this is just what the adversary desires; if he can confuse us while we are sick, it will be simpler for him to eliminate us. We are not referred to as "lone rangers," but rather as "the body of Christ." According to 1 Corinthians 12:27, "Now ye are the body of Christ, and members in particular and we are obliged to love one another as members." "A new commandment I give unto you, that ye also love one another" (John 13:34). But why should the sick call the elders of the church? Why not pray for yourself?

Calling on people to pray is, in reality, a divine concept. Jesus says in Matthew 18:18, "If any two shall agree on earth as to anything that they shall ask, it shall be done for them by our father in heaven." This is not done to cause shame, embarrassment, or gossip; rather, it is done so that you might share your burden with God's family. The elders are there to help you in any way possible. They are spiritually qualified to provide the best possible care for the sheep.

Struck By The Silent Killer

It was a major psychological and spiritual battle for me to obey James' encouragement to urgently call for the elders of the church to help me spiritually. The enemy impressed upon my mind that if I obeyed the word of God, that would be an indication that I was spiritually weak.

When James gave the directive to call, he was not suggesting that you get on the phone and call the elders every time you have a headache, an allergy, or the flu. This directive, therefore, does not apply to every sickness. The sick person James is talking about is the person who is so significantly impaired that he is unable to attend corporate fellowship.

Also, it does not mean I could not have someone else call on my behalf, but it was my responsibility to trigger the call. This can apply both to physical sickness and spiritual sickness. The New Testament is replete with references to the word "sick," which refers to someone affected by physical, emotional, spiritual, or mental illness. What was the cause of the sickness? James did not identify any particular sickness the elders should pray for, nor did he mention the cause of the sickness. At the time, I did not know what my condition was or what caused it.

What I was simply encouraged to do was to call, not just for anyone, but specifically for the elders of the church. Could anyone else have prayed and gotten the desired result? We often spend wasted time debating our God-given commands instead of acting in faith. As I pondered the scripture, my fertile mind asked, "What if I had not been born again, and what if I had no elders to call, and was not affiliated with a local assembly, would I have been in compliance with the Word? Could I have just randomly called any elders of any church?" At that point, the major benefit of being joined to a corporate body of believers made more sense to me than ever before. It also brought into focus how Satan outfoxed and isolated individuals from the church family for his own destructive purposes.

There is a clear command from God that we should not forget the assembling of ourselves to gather as the manner of some. "Not forsaking the assembling of ourselves together, as the manner of some is; but exhorting one another: and so much the more, as ye see the day approaching" (Hebrews 10:25). Many people are living in willful rebellion of that command but if we understand that sickness is a spirit from Satan, rather than a gift from God, we will do everything we can to get all of the help we need to confront our shared enemy.

I am not sure how we can demonstrate love when we separate and split ourselves, especially when it comes to not communicating the news that someone is unwell. We must bear each other's burdens, but we cannot do so if we are unaware that they have burdens.

Act of Obedience
Nonetheless, I made a firm choice to follow God's word. It seemed like an eternity from the moment I was admonished to call for the elders to pray for me to the time I mustered the confidence to obey. Although I did not personally make the call to the elders, they were notified. And although I did not ask them to come on a given day or time, information about my health was made clear to them.

I believe elders and those who received the request did pray. The instructions, on the other hand, commanded them not only to pray but also to anoint with oil. "Let them pray over him, anointing him with oil in the name of the Lord" (James 5:4).

This was not done in my case; no one prayed over me or anointed me with oil, save from my wife's prayer. However, I feel the lesson God was trying to teach me through this exercise was that when we are spiritually weak, strong spiritual leadership can benefit us, but God's divine laws must be followed to the letter.

The Lesson to Learn
It takes acquired humility of heart and mustard-seed faith in God for a sick person to profess their own inhibition and to cry out for help to those in the church. Countless others find it easier to call their health care provider in times of sickness than call church leadership. It takes active faith for church leaders to agree to pray for the recovery of a sick member of their congregation and to anoint the ill person's body with oil while praying for their healing collectively in the name of Jesus, through faith.

CHAPTER 4
Brain Attack

"And God looked at all he had made, and it was very good" (Genesis 1:31). From a human perspective, we find it hard to believe that a God who created everything "very good" would allow anything bad to happen in the world. Why would God allow a catastrophic brain damage to happen to someone?

Romans 8:28 informs individuals who have a firm belief in the Lord Jesus Christ that God is actively working in all circumstances to bring about an ultimate good. "And we know that all things work together for good to them that love God, to them who are the called according to his purpose."

God's promise that "all things work together for good" does not imply that everything that happens to us is inherently good. Obviously, some things and circumstances are unquestionably awful. God, on the other hand, understands the big picture and knows how to bring disparate elements together for the finest potential outcome.

There are no unintended consequences when it comes to God; everything happens for a reason. We do not always understand why things happen or why God allows certain unpleasant and often horrific events to occur in our lives, especially something as life-altering as a traumatic brain injury or stroke. Regardless, if we think that God has a purpose for our life and that His plan is for good rather than evil, we should embrace the occurrence and thank Him for it, including the medical team, medicine, treatment, and healing.

Struck By The Silent Killer

Christians are confronted with illnesses, accidents, and a variety of other tough and life- threatening circumstances. Each one offers us a unique opportunity to learn about God's grace and strength, at least, according to David in Psalms 119:71.

The Brain

When you consider the human body in general, and the human brain in particular—the most complex part of your body—and the enormous amount of knowledge and creativity that went into its creation, you'll agree with David when he says, "I will praise thee; for I am fearfully and wonderfully made: marvelous are thy works; and that my soul knoweth right well" (Psalms139:14).

I did not pay much attention to the brain or offer it conscious care; instead, I took its value and care for granted. The brain, on the other hand, is undoubtedly the most vital organ in the human body.

According to the **"The Human Brain,"** everything we do in our bodies is controlled by our brain, including our ability to balance, walk, speak, and consume. Our breathing, blood circulation, and heart rate are all controlled and coordinated by it. It is in charge of our ability to communicate, assess and recall information, make decisions, and experience emotions.

The nerve system's command center is the human brain, which is capable of transmitting and receiving huge volumes of data. Some doctors and scientists are still perplexed by its complexity.

There are some amazing truths about the brain that I was unaware of, and even what I did know did not have the same influence on how I treated my body as they do now. For example, I discovered that water accounts for roughly 75% of the brain. However, I had no notion that even a slight dehydration could damage concentration, memory, and other cognitive capacities (Wells). Also, according to experts, sweating for 90 minutes can decrease the brain by as much as a year of age (Scheidl). Because I was fully unaware of the possibly catastrophic consequences, I ignored adequate hydration of my body on multiple occasions. "My people are destroyed for lack of knowledge" (Hosea 4:6).

Cholesterol is also essential for learning and memory; it is a component of every brain cell, and without it, brain cells would perish. Although the brain contains 25% of the body's cholesterol, experts caution that too much cholesterol can have a range of negative implications depending on age and other factors (Björkhem & Meaney 806). This was another area of my life that had not received adequate attention until I was struck by the **"Silent Killer."**

A human brain includes close to 86 billion neurons ("How Many Neurons Are in the Brain?"), and while it cannot feel pain, it can understand pain signals transmitted to it (Greenwald). To think that there are those who adamantly declare, "There is no God." It is no surprise that God calls them fools. "The fool hath said in his heart, 'There is no God'" (Psalms 14:1).

This three-pound organ, which accounts for around 2% of a person's body weight (Raichle & Gusnard 10237), requires a steady supply of oxygen. Some brain cells can die in as little as five minutes without oxygen, resulting in catastrophic brain damage. The brain requires oxygen to function properly, much as a car requires gasoline, lubricant, braking fluid, and other components ("Cerebral Hypoxia"). It also requires carbohydrates, vitamins, minerals, exercise, sleep, and other important substances ("12 Ways to Keep Your Brain Young"). If confession is in order, I admit that I am guilty of depriving the temple, my body, of consistently and conscientiously supplying it with these essentials.

There are two main causes of stroke, a blocked artery (ischemic stroke) or the leaking or bursting of a blood vessel (hemorrhagic stroke). Some people may have only a temporary decrease in blood flow to a part of the brain, lasting as little as five minutes, without permanent damage. This is known as a transient ischemic attack (TIA) or mini-stroke ("What is a Stroke? A Mayo Clinic Expert Explains").

Ischemic Stroke
According to "What is a Stroke? A Mayo Clinic Expert Explains," staff, fatty deposits, blood clots, or other debris that travel in the bloodstream, most often from the heart, can become lodged in the blood vessels of the brain.

Struck By The Silent Killer

This narrowing or blockage of the brain's blood vessels can cause a severe reduction in blood flow, leading to the occurrence of the most common stroke, the ischemic stroke.

Also, as stated by Terry and Ludwig, "depending on the area of brain deprived of oxygen, a person may experience loss of memory, movement, or speech, or other disabilities. If blood flow is restored or pressure is relieved quickly through medical treatment, the brain may fully recover."

Reducing the Risk of a Stroke

According to experts, it is not possible to completely prevent strokes because some factors that cannot be changed such as those listed below can increase your risk of the condition ("Who Gets Vascular Dementia?"; "What is a Stroke? A Mayo Clinic Expert Explains").

(1) Age: People over 55 are more likely to suffer a stroke, however, younger people account for roughly 1 in 4 strokes.
(2) Family History: If you have a close relative who has had a stroke (parent, grandparent, brother, or sister), your risk is likely to be increased.
(3) Ethnicity: If you are South Asian, African American, or Caribbean, your stroke risk is higher, mainly because diabetes and high blood pressure are more common in these populations.
(4) Medical History: If you have ever had a TIA or a heart attack, your chances of having a stroke are increased.

However, experts claim that by simply altering your lifestyle, you can greatly lower your risk of suffering a stroke. Some critical adjustments that can be made throughout one's life to reduce the risk of a stroke or another stroke include but are not limited to maintaining a healthy cholesterol level, blood sugar level, monitor your blood pressure, and physical activity ("Risk Factors for Stroke"). These were never priorities to me before the stroke.

In terms of physical activity, I believed I was fairly active, but I now realize that I could and should have been more pro-active. Thank God for an opportunity to apply corrective measure to the destructive lifestyle I was practicing as a believer. It never ceases to amaze me how often God gives us chances to rectify our wrong behavior, yet many continue to ignore His warnings, to their peril.

The next step is to make dietary adjustments. Despite the fact that I ate well and frequently, I was malnourished. Malnutrition is a disorder that occurs when the body lacks the vitamins, minerals, and other nutrients it needs to keep its tissues and organs healthy ("Malnutrition"). When I first heard the word "malnutrition," I immediately thought of undernutrition, which happens when vital nutrients are not taken in sufficient quantities or are eliminated faster than they can be supplied (Morley).

Then there's obesity, which is a major problem for many people; an estimated 1.9 billion people are overweight or obese with 462 million underweight ("What is Malnutrition?"). That is a staggering figure. Despite the fact that I was never statistically overweight, maintaining a healthy body was not always considered a major preventative measure against stroke or other illnesses for me.

It is vital to take care of your body because you only have one. You cannot entrust its care to someone else; you are responsible for knowing everything there is to know about it, as well as your family's medical history. Again, I do not want to sound like an expert because this is a major learning process for me.

Suffering is one of the numerous topics addressed in scripture; in this life, we will all experience suffering to some degree or the other. Individuals who are living with or know someone who has suffered from a traumatic brain injury must demonstrate to him or her the everyday love, grace, and mercy that God provides to us. This can be accomplished by offering essential spiritual, emotional, and physical assistance, which will satisfy the Lord. "And let us not be weary in well doing: for in due season we shall reap, if we faint not" (Galatians 6:9).

Victory in Jesus
We all want to live victorious lives in all areas of our life, including good health. Believers in Jesus Christ especially are expected to walk in the victory that has already been secured for us according to 1 Corinthians 15:57, "But thanks be to God, which giveth us the victory through our Lord Jesus Christ." Acting on God's word and trusting in Him is the surest way to grow one's faith and walk in victory.

Struck By The Silent Killer

For example, before facing Goliath the giant in battle, David reflected on his earlier victories, which included God empowering him to slay both a lion and a bear without even using a slingshot. These events undoubtedly fueled his determination to take on what many would consider a monumental task. We know from reading the Bible that the outcome was a colossal victory over the giant and his people.

Through this stroke experience as well as David's experiences, God is teaching me so many lessons. The most fundamental one is this, "My faith in God will always bring positive results when it is applied to God's word through Jesus Christ." Jesus not only has the capacity and authority to forgive sins and heal, but He also has the ability to heal strokes and any other illnesses or disease that may be present.

On one occasion, Jesus visited a home in Capernaum. He was giving a lecture to a big crowd when he was interrupted by four determined men who brought their paralyzed comrade on a stretcher to Jesus for healing. Nobody knows what caused his disability or how long he was bedridden.

Notwithstanding, when they were not able to get the man through the door, they dug a hole in the roof and lowered him down on the stretcher to Jesus. When Jesus observed their faith, He healed the man and forgave his sins. Mark 2 contains this magnificent example of what faith in Jesus can accomplish.

As you exercise your faith, it grows stronger, allowing you to achieve larger successes. I believe God is preparing me to serve in this area now and in the future. We are all called to minister healing to the sick and afflicted. He wants us to release His creative healing power through the Holy Spirit, in His name.

On one occasion, when Jesus sent forth His disciples, He told them to "heal the sick, cleanse the lepers, raise the dead, cast out devils" (Matthew 10:8). Today, I believe He is saying the same thing to us. If you are a believer in Jesus Christ, and you are suffering from a brain injury or another illness or condition, I feel He is speaking to you: "...[He] took our infirmities, and bore our sickness" (Matthew 8:17).

CHAPTER 5
Facts About Stroke

P hysical symptoms are among the most common, despite the fact that strokes normally hit without warning. I did not treat the weakness in my left leg as a sign that my brain's blood supply had been limited or was being diminished since I did not identify any of the symptoms.

I did not pay attention to so many things. When I moved around before the stroke, I did not give a second thought to how my brain needs to coordinate information from my eyes and or that it is the balance system to controlling muscles and joints in my body. I agree with the King David when he said, "I will praise thee; for because I am fearfully and wonderfully made: marvellous are thy works; and that my soul knoweth right well" (Psalms 139:14).

After a stroke, moving around and maintaining balance requires extra concentration, which can feel like a full day's work. For example, if I am walking and conversing at the same time, I may need to stop walking to listen or speak.

Because of my left leg's weakness, it is more difficult for me to keep my balance, increasing my risks of tripping, slipping, and falling. Standing and walking in a fluid motion without thinking about it is the most difficult thing for me. Strokes are a serious medical condition. They have the ability to harm, paralyze, and kill individuals. In 2020, 1 in 6 deaths from cardiovascular disease was due to stroke according to "Stroke Statistics".

Struck By The Silent Killer

It is documented that in the United States around 795,000 strokes occur each year, and I am unfortunately one of them. Stroke is also the fifth most common cause of death. A stroke occurs every 40 seconds in the United States and kills someone every 3.5 minutes. And it is one of the primary causes of long-term impairment ("Stroke Statistics").

Additional facts that are just as startling is that "stroke is a leading cause of death for Americans, but the risk of having a stroke varies with race and ethnicity. Also, the risk of having a first stroke is nearly twice as high for Blacks as for Whites, and Blacks have the highest rate of death due to stroke" ("Stroke Statistics").

It is speculated that the majority of persons who have suffered a stroke or another serious disease are reluctant to discuss it. The reasons can be varied. A stroke can cause significant personality changes in addition to any obvious physical aftereffects ("Stroke: Emotional & Behavioral Changes"). It can be difficult for the stroke victim to comprehend the changes let alone to articulate them to others.

Stroke is preventable, treatable, and defeatable. As mentioned earlier, a stroke, sometimes known as a "brain attack," is a leading cause of long-term disability in adults. Patients who are willing to monitor their blood pressure and cholesterol levels can prevent 80% of strokes. In addition, factors such as excessive amount consumption, frequent smoking, and lack of exercise, can also contribute to a stroke ("Brain").

People of all ages, religions, sexual orientations, genders, socioeconomic statuses, and political ideas are equally affected by a stroke. Studies show that just 40% of men who have a stroke die as a result, compared to 60% of women. In addition, men and women experience different stroke signs and symptoms. Stroke also claims the lives of twice as many women as breast cancer each year. And African-American women experience strokes at a far higher incidence than Caucasian women ("More Women Die from Stroke Than Men").

People are impacted differently by strokes depending on where they happen in the brain and how much brain tissue is affected.

Muscle control, mobility, thinking, memory, and speech are just a few of the things they can affect ("Effects of Stroke").

The brain is separated into left and right hemispheres, with the left controlling the right side of the body and the right controlling the left. Our brain controls everything we do in our bodies, including our capacity to balance, move, talk, and eat. It is in charge of controlling and coordinating our breathing, blood circulation, and heart rate. It controls our ability to process and remember information, make decisions, and feel emotions ("Brain").

Just as a car requires gasoline, lubricant, brake fluid, and other components to function properly, the brain requires adequate blood flow to function properly. The brain requires specific nutrients such as glucose, vitamins, minerals, exercise, sleep, and other important compounds to function properly (Chudler).

God's most perplexing and mysterious creation must be this three-pound wonder known as the brain. It is a puzzle. I often wonder why God would hold man in such extraordinarily high regard. Why did he place him above all of his labors' fruits? It is mind-boggling to consider that there are some people who treat this unique God with nothing but contempt and disrespect. I do not believe the world's greatest scientists can or will ever know for certain the full potential of the human brain. It is indeed an enigma.

Symptoms of Mini-Strokes

Dizziness, awful migraines, inability to smile, slurred speech, blurred vision and vision loss, speech loss, weakness or numbness on one side of the body, and other symptoms have been reported by people who claim to have had a stroke ("What is a Stroke? A Mayo Clinic Expert Explains"). One of the symptoms I had was a heavy sensation in my left leg, which made it difficult for me to walk normally. Following a stroke, some people lose their ability to read, swallow, write, count, speak, walk, or run ("What is a Stroke? A Mayo Clinic Expert Explains"). Also, following a stroke, some of the things we take for granted on a daily basis, like money, become meaningless.

Struck By The Silent Killer

I am convinced that God allows certain things to happen to every one of His children, including a stroke. However, this does not imply that He is to blame. Many things happen to us that we may never fully comprehend; but we can be confident that if we trust God, He will use even our worst tragedies for good.

Some people may not believe it is appropriate to question God about something that is happening or has happened to them of which they are unaware. Personally, I do not feel it is necessarily wrong; nevertheless, if we understand and embrace the validity of the Bible, we will know that all things work together for the good of those who love God. You may ask, "When there is suffering and grief in the world, how can everything work together for good?"

People who love God and are chosen for His purposes are warned that they will experience things like poverty, reproach, wealth, losses, gains, dishonor, anguish, honor, contentment, and scorn, as well as health problems, strokes, and possibly a billion other changes throughout their lives. All of these combined are for his good.

"And we know that all things work together for good to them that love God, to them who are the called according to his purpose" (Romans 8:28).

Five Types of Strokes
Strokes are medical emergencies that occur when blood flow to the brain is stopped or interrupted. There are five different kinds of strokes: Ischemic Stroke, Hemorrhagic Stroke, Transient Ischemic Attack (Mini-Stroke), Brain Stem Stroke, and Cryptogenic Stroke, a stroke of an unknown cause ("Types of Stroke").

Mini-strokes, also known as transient ischemic events (TIA), are a type of stroke that occurs in a short period of time. The carotid arteries, which provide blood to the brain and head, can get clogged with plaque, and oxygen cannot reach the brain, resulting in a stroke ("Carotid Artery Disease"). This is precisely what happened to me.

A larger stroke might result in permanent speech loss, one-sided paralysis, or death ("Stroke: Overview") On the other hand, my TIA left me with some weakness in my left leg, which is improving with hard work and perseverance.

One of the most difficult aspects of a stroke is assessing whether or not you will fully recover. You never know what the future holds, or if things will get back to normal.

A stroke can affect every aspect of your life and result in permanent disability. The long-term repercussions of a stroke are determined by which section of the brain was affected and how much damage was done ("Effects of Stroke").

The region of the brain that helps with communication, such as speech, writing, and reading, may be injured in certain persons. Among other reasons, they may struggle to find the correct words or understand what others are saying ("Effects of Stroke"). It is tough to communicate when there is a gap between the brain and the lips; the words are there, but the ability to speak is not.

Physical symptoms are among the most common, despite the fact that strokes normally hit without warning. It is estimated that eight out of ten people who have had a stroke will experience muscle weakness on one side of their body, usually in one arm or leg. This weakness can range from minor to severe ("Post-Stroke Challenges"). When a person cannot move one or more limbs at all, it is a more serious weakness. I did not treat the weakness in my left leg as a sign that my brain's blood supply had been limited or was being diminished since I did not identify any of the symptoms. Because my circumstances could have been far worse, I will be eternally grateful to God. A stroke-affected area on the right side of my brain caused only minor paralysis in my left leg. Multiple disorders, such as difficulty retaining or grasping objects, can be brought on by muscle weakness ("Improving Fine Motor Skills"). Possible negative consequences also include mood swings, hopelessness, tension, and concentration deficits (Rao). One difficulty I experience is that I become tired after standing for a long period.

Struck By The Silent Killer

Not only may a stroke affect every aspect of your life, but it can also cause changes in daily routine. It might have an impact on the living situation as well as sexual connections. It can be an infringement on independence and so much more such as handling difficult skills like driving or working.

As a stroke (TIA) survivor, the most difficult aspect for me is needing to be constantly conscious of the emotional and personality changes that seem to lurk around every corner. When I am thinking to myself, "Why me? What did I do wrong?" the Holy Spirit always comforts me. Psalms 119:71 is one of the verses He frequently reminds me of, "It is good for me that I have been afflicted; that I might learn thy statutes."

CHAPTER 6
At Church

When I went to bed that night, I was disappointed because my leg had not healed, and my walking abilities had deteriorated. I did not tell my wife how I was feeling since, after 40 years of marriage, I was like an open book to her. However, she had no idea that I had vowed to spend the following three days fasting and praying at the church's altar, and that I would not leave until I was healed.

A fantastic lesson in Matthew 17 influenced my decision in wanting to stay at the church until I received my healing. The lesson explains that on one particular occasion, when Jesus was away, a father approached the disciples and asked them to heal his sick son. The disciples attempted to heal the boy but were unable. Jesus and three of his disciples who had accompanied him to a mountaintop arrived and saw the large crowd. According to Matthew 17:14, we read "...There came to him a certain man, kneeling down to him, and saying," 'Lord, have mercy on my son: for he is lunatick, and sore vexed: for ofttimes he falleth into the fire, and oft into the water.'"

As a parent and now a grandfather, the story of this troubled young man has always touched me deeply. I often pondered what it must have been like for the father to witness his son being mistreated by that demonic spirit. It is obvious that the youngster had no control over his actions. The boy was taken to the disciples, which made this story even more heartbreaking because, regrettably, many people who seek assistance from the church today are turned away disappointed.

This father must have been disappointed when the disciples were unable to heal his son. In my mind's eye, I can see him begging for his son's deliverance from the powers of Satan while prostrate on the ground, unaffected by the large group that was present. Without a doubt, he was prepared to go above and beyond to show his child the love of a father.

The father's most heartfelt prayer was "Lord, have mercy on my son." We do not deserve God's favors. As a just reward for our sin, we are entitled to sickness, disease, and death. But God our loving Father sent His son Jesus to take the punishment for our sins. As a result, this father is showing us that if we accept who Jesus is and approach Him in humility and ask for mercy, He will hear and respond to our petition.

"And I brought him to thy disciples, and they could not cure him," he said to Jesus (Matthew 17:16). But he was factually false when he told Jesus that "they could not cure him." Despite the disciple's attempts to treat his son's failing, it was not because "they could not." Unfortunately, this father's rhetoric had affected the disciples. Jesus described these onlookers as "O faithless and perverse generation" (Matthew 17:17), as this group, comprised of the father of the child, those that were with him, and the Scribes that were present, disputed with the disciples.

The Bible tells us that "…Jesus rebuked the devil; and he departed out of him: and the child was cured from that very hour" (Matthew 17:18). After Jesus healed the lad, they went to Jesus in private and asked why they had not been successful in their healing mission. "Why could not we cast him out?" (Matthew 17:19). They were probably angered by Jesus' comments. "And Jesus said unto them, Because of your unbelief." Yet He also revealed the key to their victory over the condition or spirit that was holding this lad captive: "Howbeit this kind goeth not out but by prayer and fasting" (Matthew 17:21).

Jesus did not tell his disciples that it was not His will for the lad to be healed, nor did He tell them that the demon was far too powerful in His response to their question. I take Jesus' statement to suggest that they would be unstoppable if they had faith and combined it with prayer and fasting.

Struck By The Silent Killer

In the morning, my condition had become a serious source of anxiety for me and my family; I had not gotten a decent night's sleep as I found myself testing my weighted leg at various points throughout the night, hoping for normalcy.

As the sun rose higher in the sky, it seemed as if the enemy's voices were waiting to attack me in greater numbers than the day before. Throughout the night, my condition had deteriorated significantly. The voices I thought I had drowned out with scriptures had erupted in a volcanic eruption. I requested Angela to drive me to the church since I discovered my left leg had lost all power and I could not put any pressure on it like I could the day before. Throughout it all, the only place I could imagine myself going was to the church, where I could envision myself sprawled out at the altar praying to the God I know to be a Healer.

With the help of a "u-walker" and my concerned wife, I made it to the car and to the church. When we arrived at the church, my wife made me a hot drink, and I positioned my prayer mat on the altar. I was ready to seek divine healing, even if it would take three days. Three days was a random number that came to me; it had nothing to do with any specific command from God.

I laid out before the alter and prayed after anointing myself with oil. I noticed that someone had joined me at the altar not long after. The individual was humming a melody, which I overheard. She was one of our pastors who had come to pray for me in obedience to my request for the elders to pray.

After we exchanged greetings, the person inquired as to what had occurred. I recounted the incident to the best of my recollection. "Have you checked your blood pressure?" the minister inquired. That was a strange question to me.

I was taken aback and snapped back in surprise "My blood pressure?" "Yes, your blood pressure," said the pastor. My response was, "No, I haven't checked my pressure."

Victory Over Stroke

I did not make it a practice to check my blood pressure. In fact, it had been years since I had had my blood or anything else checked.

She got the blood pressure machine wrapped around my arm in no time, like an expert. I heard a noise and felt the cuff expand. "What if this thing bursts?" I recalled thinking. The instrument began to deflate till it stopped while that and other things ran through my mind.

"Your pressure is 208 over 105. Let's go!" remarked the minister, almost astounded. High blood pressure is defined as a reading of 130-139 systolic or 80-89 diastolic mm Hg or higher ("Understanding Blood Pressure Readings").

Excessive blood pressure affects 1 out 3 people, generally developing in the late 30s and early 40s. As the "Silent Killer," high blood pressure can cause major health problems such as heart attacks, heart failure, strokes, and kidney damage, if left untreated or uncontrolled ("High Blood Pressure–Understanding the Silent Killer").

"Go where?" I responded, a smirk on my face and a small chuckle in my voice. "To the hospital," she said, her eyes widening in surprise. "To the hospital?" I inquired, as if I hadn't heard. "Yes, to the hospital. Let's go, buddy!" "Which one?" I inquired. "Anyone! Let's go!" she exclaimed.

I could not believe what was happening to me, the pastor. It was as if I could hear people passing all sorts of negative criticisms. These thoughts were demoralizing. The seriousness of my condition was now beginning to hit home. The enormity of my predicament was beginning to dawn on me.

CHAPTER 7
At the Hospital

Nevertheless, I decided to go to the hospital without hesitation. The minister assisted me in getting into her vehicle and to the hospital. I was escorted into the hospital when I arrived. Once inside, I was seen by congenial professionals, to whom I had to recite what transpired.

The Big Announcement

My wife had arrived at the hospital by this time, having been informed of the results of my blood pressure reading. After a long list of questions and what appeared to be endless medical tests, I was then seen by a doctor, who informed me that I had experienced "a small stroke, a TIA," in a very pleasant manner. "A stroke, you say?" I inquired, not really comprehending the gravity of the situation until I was told, "We are going to have to admit you."

I felt as if I had had an out of body experience at the time, and I could not believe what I was hearing. I had never been a big admirer of hospitals, despite working in one for a while, and I had no idea what a "stroke" was. I had heard the word and knew people who had had strokes, but I never imagined I would be a part of the stroke statistics.

Consider how different the world would be if everyone who has dedicated their life to serving humanity as medical staff did not exist; I am grateful to God for everyone who works in the health-care industry.

Struck By The Silent Killer

Instantaneously my heart began to race rapidly as my busy imagination picked me up and transported me away to various wards of the hospital, where I imagined individuals in beds, connected up to various devices, some of whom appeared to be in agonizing pain and crying for assistance. I was immediately transported back to my first and only other personal hospital experience, which occurred over forty years ago in London, England.

Everything began to come into focus in my mind when I was told to sit in the wheelchair so the attendant could take me to my room, where I would be held "for observation." From wherever I was in la-la-land, I soon snapped back to reality.

I was about to leave for my allocated ward when I was informed that owing to COVID-19 no one but staff could accompany me. Angela, my wife, and Pastor Hilma Tucker, who had been by my side since taking my blood pressure, ordering that we go to the hospital, and accompanying me to her car, were both unable to go with me to the room.

As I was being wheeled down the corridors of the hospital, I remember reciting these scripture verses from 1 Thessalonians 5:18, "In everything give thanks: for this is the will of God in Christ Jesus concerning you," and Romans 8:28, "And we know that all things work together for good to them that love God, to them who are the called according to his purpose." The nurse in charge received and greeted me kindly when I arrived on the assigned floor. At my request, the bed they had originally assigned me was changed to a window bed, which helped to settle feelings I could not explain.

My two days in the hospital were eye-opening; I was exposed to the human body's magnificent anatomy in ways I never would have imagined if it had not been for the stroke. I realized that I was only kidding myself when I said I was caring for my physique. I had no idea how dangerous a poor diet could be. It was now no surprise what David declared in Psalms 119:71, "It is good for me that I have been afflicted; that I might learn thy statutes."

Victory Over Stroke

The doctor who told me I had had "a small stroke" came to that decision after performing a CTS scan on my brain. A computed tomography scan (CTS) is a process that creates a succession of in-depth images of various body parts using an x-ray machine connected to a computer. To see tissues and organs in three dimensions (3-D), various angles of photographs are used. To make the tissues and organs more visible, a dye may be ingested or injected into a vein. Using a CT scan can aid in disease diagnosis, therapy planning, and monitoring the effectiveness of treatment (Brazier).

Prior to this experience I had heard much about it, but I never stopped to wonder about the functionality of this contraption. After I was given the diagnosis, I asked God to forgive me for not taking better care of my body, His temple. Then he reminded me of His word in Hosea 4:6. "My people are destroyed for lack of knowledge." And if we lack wisdom, we are encouraged to request it. "If any of you lack wisdom, let him ask of God, that giveth to all men liberally, and upbraideth not; and it shall be given him" (James 1:5).

I was not always as consistent as I told myself in pursuing excellent health. The diet I followed proved this to be true. How frequently do we trick ourselves into believing we are taking the greatest possible care of our health when all we are really doing is lying to ourselves. Nothing is worse than "self-lies," which are immensely worse than other people lying to you.

God most likely advised me at some point to keep an eye on my blood pressure and limit certain foods, but I disobeyed him for unknown reasons. We are told in scriptures "that if we ask anything according to His will He heareth us" (1 John 5:14). So, by me asking for wisdom I was asking according to His will. One of many things could have caused God not to hear or answer. For example, if there was or is wrongdoing or sin in my heart, then God promised not to hear. "If I regard iniquity in my heart, the Lord will not hear me" (Psalms 66:18).

I declare I committed a sin by failing to take the greatest care of my health. However, God will always give His children what they need if it is in accordance with His will since He is a prayer- answering God.

Struck By The Silent Killer

As a result, if we ask God for knowledge in all areas of our lives and are willing to follow His instructions, He will show us where to go, how to adjust our lifestyle, when and what medications to take, and other crucial health and life-related steps.

According to His word, the God who created us intends for us to be healthy and prosperous on many levels. "Beloved, I wish above all things that thou mayest prosper and be in health, even as thy soul prospereth," John writes in 3 John 3:2. One who is adored is said to be "beloved." As a result, it is clear to whom He is writing. All people who have accepted our Creator God's Son, Jesus Christ, are adored by Him and are referred to be His off-spring. Following His directions like any obedient child would do, is far more priceless than material prosperity and excellent health. We must treat the things we most frequently lust for as transient benefits.

John 10:27, on the other hand, reveals what God desires for us. "My sheep hear my voice, and I know them, and they follow me." He craves a relationship with His children and wants them to obey Him. "And I will give them eternal life, and they will never die," (John 10:28); here He guarantees eternal life when His criteria are met.

If others lack wisdom, those who are called "My people" by God should not lack it, especially since they are told that their bodies are God's temple. "What? Know ye not that your body is the temple of the Holy Ghost which is in you, which ye have of God, and ye are not your own?" (1 Corinthians 6:19).

CHAPTER 8

High Cholesterol

H igh cholesterol cannot be felt or seen, making it tough to diagnose. Many people do not know that having high blood cholesterol raises the risk of developing heart disease, the number one killer, and stroke, the number five killer. Even more troubling is the fact that you may be affected, along with about 38% of adults and 7% of American adolescents between the ages of 6 and 19 ("High Cholesterol Facts").

How would you know if you have high cholesterol since it has no symptoms? According to experts, a cholesterol checkup should be performed every 4 to 6 years for healthy individuals because there are no signs or indicators of high cholesterol ("Getting Your Cholesterol Checked"). As a result, those with heart disease, diabetes, and a family history of high cholesterol ought to have their cholesterol checked more frequently. Let me also remind you of what God said in Hosea 4:6: "My people are destroyed for lack knowledge."

I had extremely high cholesterol, which a simple blood test would have revealed, but I had never sought medical advice before. If I had known and heeded this warning, it is possible I could have been spared from being struck by the **"Silent Killer."** It is possible you may not have considered this before as well.

Victory Over Stroke

There are times when someone in the know tries to alert us to a danger that is about to strike, but we choose to ignore them until it is too late. That has happened to me numerous times. In response, King Solomon said, "A wise man will hear, and he will increase learning; and a man of understanding shall attain wise counsels" (Proverbs1:5).

Although the term "high cholesterol" is one that the majority of people are familiar with, it is my opinion that only few people, including me, truly understand what it implies.

There are two sources of cholesterol. All the necessary cholesterol is produced in your liver. The remaining cholesterol in the body is obtained from animal-based diets. For instance, dairy products, pork, and poultry all include dietary cholesterol ("What is Cholesterol?").

Packaged and processed meals that are fried and battered have a lot of saturated and trans fats, terms which were unfamiliar to me. The liver produces more cholesterol as a result of these fats and some people see a change in their cholesterol level from healthy to unhealthy as a result of the increased production ("Facts About Trans Fats").

When the body has too much cholesterol, it can build up inside the blood vessels, making it difficult for blood to circulate through them. This can eventually lead to heart disease. In addition, high cholesterol can affect everyone, regardless of weight or level of exercise, but those who are overweight are at a significantly higher risk ("Facts About Trans Fats"). Once more, if I had not suffered a stroke, it is unlikely that I would have paid this crucial topic such close attention. If you will heed my warning and at the very least get your blood checked, it will be worthwhile, even if Satan had intended it for my demise.

"I will praise thee," King David declared, "for I am fearfully and wonderfully made: wondrous are thy works; and that my soul knows well" (Psalms 139:14). David recognized the fact that neither he nor his parents had formed him, but it was God who had done it, and he expressed his thankfulness by saying, "I will praise thee," or "I will offer thee thanks for forming me in such a magnificent fashion."

Struck By The Silent Killer

Those who have spent a lifetime studying the human anatomy are awe-struck by the perfection, exact symmetry, and proportion of all of its parts, as well as their position and functionality. Every bone, muscle, artery, neuron, and fiber are beautifully crafted from earth's dust. The ear is for hearing and the eye is for seeing. All of this demonstrates God's wisdom and intelligence.

Although we cannot see God, we know He can see us; this awareness of His being and deeds should bring us from a point of admiration to a feeling of holy dread, honor, love, appreciation, and thanksgiving. When we are totally convinced that God created us in a way that distinguishes us from inanimate objects and brute creation, our souls will be overflowing with thankfulness, and we will pay closer attention to the body He has given us to live in.

I had been hearing practically nonstop talk about good and bad cholesterol for years, but it was always perplexing and convoluted because no one seems to agree on anything. For example, soon after one expert provides numbers strongly and "scientifically" indicating that an item is bad for our cholesterol, another informs us of a new body of research that shows the exact same product is what the body requires for optimal health. I am not sure who is credible, or whether I should question "who stands to earn the most financially." I cannot help but believe that money plays a role in some of these conclusions. Regardless, I believe that the ideal nourishment is that which was established by Creator God in Genesis 1:29, "Behold, I have given you every herb bearing seed that is on the face of all the world, and every tree in which is the fruit of a tree yielding seed; it shall be for meat to you." To me, a non-medical, non-nutritionally certified person, it is evident that the things you eat affect your cholesterol level for better or worse. God's plan for optimal health and vital processes like hormone generation and cell development calls for the presence of cholesterol. To achieve this, He has given the right nutrients.

We all want our hearts to be healthy, and we all know how important a healthy heart is for living a prosperous, happy, healthy, and long life. However, our efforts to maintain this standard are not always given the attention they deserve, or perhaps I should speak for myself.

Nevertheless, I firmly believe that with discipline and a desire to live a healthy life, the changes that are required will be a small price to pay. That important first step could start with getting your blood levels checked by your medical team. Unfortunately, I am not qualified to advise on what foods should be consumed in order to achieve the proper cholesterol levels for anyone.

I can, however, tell you what God instructed Adam and Eve to consume. Because God commanded, "...Every herb bearing seed, which is upon the face of all the earth, and every tree, in the which is the fruit of a tree yielding seed; to you it shall be for meat." Even if others would disagree, I am confident that none but the body's Maker and Creator knows what is best for the human body.

CHAPTER 9
High Blood Pressure

O ne of the sneakiest and riskiest medical diseases is referred to as hypertension. The **"Silent Killer"** and high blood pressure are other names for it.

How does blood pressure work? It is the force that pushes blood past the artery walls in your body. But too much pressure can harden the arteries, reducing the amount of blood and oxygen reaching the heart. This can lead to an irregular heartbeat which can then lead to sudden death ("What is High Blood Pressure?").

Your risk of acquiring high blood pressure is increasing unless you can go back in time. This is because risk rises with age (Jaret). However, until the heart and arteries have been seriously injured, high blood pressure typically shows no signs.

Worldwide statistics estimate that about 1.3 billion people suffer with hypertension and nearly 46% with this **"Silent Killer"** are fully ignorant of it. It is also the leading cause of death globally, accounting for more than half of all fatalities caused by heart disease and stroke ("Hypertension"). Thus, it is vital that people regularly have their blood pressure checked.

Struck By The Silent Killer

Although the greatest way to determine how healthy your blood pressure is through routine checkups, it had been a while since I had my blood pressure taken. This was partly because I had no symptoms and, from what I could tell, I was in rather decent health.

In fact, years may go by while you have high blood pressure with no signs or symptoms, unless it is very severe. A heart attack, a stroke, heart failure, kidney disease, and other significant health issues are therefore more likely to occur if high blood pressure is left unchecked, untreated, and unregulated ("Hypertension").

This absence of symptoms in hypertension is one of its most worrisome elements. However, there may be certain indications to watch out for if your blood pressure is exceedingly high. These include but are not limited to experiencing headaches, shortness of breath, nosebleeds, anxiety, stress, lack of sleep, exhaustion, chest discomfort, tremors, nausea, ringing in the ears, distorted speech, forgetfulness, blood in the urine, vision issues, or a pounding in the chest, neck, or ear ("Hypertension").

Although it can be self-monitored at home to determine how your blood changes throughout the day, regular visits with your doctor are the best approach to determine if your blood pressure is excessive. You can also work with your doctor to control high blood pressure if you are aware that you have it.

It has been determined that my TIA stroke was primarily caused by excessive blood pressure and high cholesterol. After hearing such information, I sincerely asked God to pardon me for this awful act of negligence. The church, which the world should rush to like a hospital for healing, is frequently troubled by the exponential increase in the number of pastors and parishioners who suffer from chronic illnesses like high blood pressure, cancer, and heart disease, to name a few. Without a doubt, many people have prayed, "Lord, please heal me of high blood pressure or anything." In response, God might have asked, if they could hear His voice, "When will you obey me by making dietary changes and starting an exercise regimen?"

Repentance is expected of everyone, including Christians. Some might question what it means to repent. It is a decision an individual makes to quit acting in a way that violates God's commands and a deliberate change of behavior or conduct. Healing might occur when we begin acting obediently in the areas where we have been disobedient.

Not only do we need to repent of crimes like adultery and formication, but also any other sin that violates one of God's commandments. Jesus said in John 8:32, "And ye shall know the truth, and the truth shall make you free." Once we "know" the truth, we must obey it since it is only through obedience to the truth that we shall be set free. Although Jesus was referring to Himself as the truth, any known truth about our creation can make us free. Many of us would prefer to place the blame somewhere else than take responsibility for our health issues, much like Adam did in the Garden of Eden. Instead of turning from his sin. Genesis 3:12 states, "And the man said, "The woman whom thou gavest to be with me, she gave me of the tree, and I did eat."" He made no effort to repent of his sinful act of disobeying the command of his Creator, God. God had commanded and promised him, "But of the tree of the knowledge of good and evil, thou shalt not eat of it: for in the day that thou eatest thereof thou shalt surely die" (Genesis 2:17).

There are certain things we have absolutely no control over such as our genetic make-up, the aging process, or our ethnicity. On the other hand, there are other factors related to high blood pressure that we can influence, including our weight, exercise habits, and the food we consciously eat.

The most frequent causes of high blood pressure, according to experts, include heredity, aging, psychosocial stress, obesity, diabetes, insulin resistance, alcohol misuse, a sedentary lifestyle, high salt intake, and low potassium intake ("Causes of High Blood Pressure"). I discovered after being struck by the "Silent Killer" that I was predisposed because of my relationship to a very close family member. Although my doctor had determined that my affliction was caused by high blood pressure, it is also highly likely that other contributing factors included stress, aging, low potassium, and perhaps even sleep depravity and dehydration.

Struck By The Silent Killer

When I was given a high blood pressure diagnosis, I repented of my sin and decided to live a repentant lifestyle, which means that I now understand that taking care of my health is my responsibility and that God has given me insight into how to be a good steward of His temple. I have learned from the experience that there are several strategies I can employ to achieve this objective. Among them, but not exclusively, is keeping an eye on my weight. Weight loss is one of the most effective methods for lowering blood pressure, according to experts, because blood pressure frequently rises when weight, especially around the waist, increases ("10 Ways to Control High Blood Pressure Without Medication").

Another fantastic method is regular exercise. I was not a couch potato, but I was not as disciplined with my workouts as I am today. At the moment, I work out at least four hours a week. The "Silent Killer" can come back if you give in, therefore, I want to stay constant.

I have planned my diet to include a lot of whole grains, fruits, and veggies, with little dairy. Returning to the diet that God supplied to the first man in Genesis 1:29 is my ultimate goal. "And God said, 'Behold, I have given you every herb bearing seed, which is upon the face of all the earth, and every tree, in the which is the fruit of a tree yielding seed; to you it shall be for meat.'"

God, who is fully aware of our physical limitations, did not promise us avoidance of experiencing stressful situations. But rather He instructed us on how to handle them when they occurred, rather than if they did, and explained why: "Casting all your care upon him; for he careth for you." (1 Peter 5:7).

Stress causes hormonal imbalances in our bodies, which can lead to increased heart rates and blood flow, both of which are risky while our bodies are at rest. God does not want us to turn to our comfort foods while we are going through terrible times, instead, He wants us to come to Him. Whether we lose a family member or experience health problems, financial difficulties, or challenging assignments, He wants us to depend on Him for everything.

Victory Over Stroke

Your health can be harmed by high blood pressure in a number of ways. Important organs including your heart, brain, kidneys, and eyes might suffer severe damage ("What is Hypertension? A Mayo Clinic Expert Explains"). I thank God that none of my organs were harmed by the high levels of my blood pressure, as reported by my medical team. I think God has given us many chances to change certain actions. Some are warnings that Satan, the devil, that thief who comes only to steal, kill, and destroy, will have access to carry out his destructive task if remedial steps are not taken and the door that is left open is not closed.

I implore you to pray to God about any significant health issues you may be experiencing, including heart attack, stroke, heart failure, and kidney failure, not only because He cares but also because He has promised to go above and beyond our expectations. "Now unto him that is able to do exceeding abundantly above all that we ask or think" (Ephesians 3:20). Once we have a complete understanding of the Supreme Creator, I pray that we will begin to treat our bodies with the reverence and care that He will find pleasing. Having incomplete information can be harmful, even when done with good intentions. "My people are destroyed for lack of knowledge: because thou hast rejected knowledge, I will also reject thee" (Hosea 4:6).

CHAPTER 10
Who Has Legal Rights to My Body?

N o one who professes to follow Jesus Christ will dispute that God has commanded them to spread the gospel to every nation on earth as a result of their adherence to His word, and no one will contest that God also wants that vessel to be in good health.

"Surrender" is characterized as the act of conceding to another person's authority or giving up ownership of something. This is similar to the legal transfer of ownership that occurs when two parties sign a document transferring ownership of a piece of property, for example, from one party to another. Nothing or no one at all can be used by God unless they are completely surrendered to Him and His purpose. Surrendering to God, demonstrates one's entire trust in Him, His abilities and belief in His promises.

God expects individuals who bear His name to relinquish daily and moment-to-moment authority over their lives. The toughest thing to do, though, is to relinquish control of anything, particularly of oneself, because doing so leaves us feeling vulnerable. Giving yourself completely over to God shows that you have faith in everything that He can do for you and through you according to what He has promised.

Struck By The Silent Killer

While they were casting a net into the sea, Jesus invited Peter and his brother Andrew to follow him, promising that He would make them fishers of men. In Matthew 4:19, "...he saith unto them, 'Follow me, and I will make you fishers of men'" Both brothers immediately "left their nets, and followed him" (Matthew 4:20).

However, Peter and the others most likely did not fully grasp what was expected of them. I believe Peter was looking forward to gaining some physical benefits in return for giving up his profession as a fisherman. He was not thinking of spiritual gain after this life. He wanted his stuff in the now. As it is for so many people today, Peter's yielding was likely motivated by the possibility of personal gain.

Peter reminded Jesus on one occasion that they had abandoned everything to follow him, as follows: "Then Peter began to say unto him, Lo, we have left all, and have followed thee" (Mark 10:28.). But it appears that Jesus needed to clarify to Peter and the others that the submission He had called them to was not solely for the benefit of what they would gain from it, but that the major incentive was "for my sake, and the gospel's" (Mark 10:29). Did they realize how important the commitment was they were being asked to make? When we give ourselves over to God, is He demanding all of our time, all of our resources, or just some? He is not asking any less of us now than He did of them in terms of giving up control of our lives. But do we truly understand what is He is asking?

I would not be telling the truth if I say that I am always yielding in all areas of my life, even as a man of God. However, my burning desire is to fully commit my life in totality to the Holy Spirit. Yes, I am born again, but there are greater and deeper depths that I desire to attain in God, which requires greater surrender. And because my burning desire is to seek to please God, I must beg the Holy Spirit to point out any sin in my life which would cause a blockage to total surrender. I must also ask His forgiveness of whatever I am fully aware of as offenses or iniquity.

I believe that true submission is becoming so self-submissive that I become more God-centered and less self-centered. Instead of saying, "....Behold, we have forsaken all, and followed thee; what shall we have therefore?"

as Peter did when he approached Jesus, I would rather to say, "God, I'm coming to You just because You're who You are, even if I gain no material wealth in this life, and even my life is endangered." What about you? Are you certain that you are as submissive as God desires, or merely as you believe you should be?

As a result of complete surrender, personal rewards are guaranteed. For example, I should not approach God and say, "Lord, I give myself to you, and I want to be made holy." Being rescued from sin and made holy are promises to individuals who are in good standing with God. "But seek first the kingdom of God and his righteousness," Jesus said. What did He say should come first? He said, "...the kingdom of God, and his righteousness" (Matthew 6:33). Is He still required to fulfill His promised benefits of "...and all these things shall be added unto you," if His kingdom is not sought first?

In my mind, I have always desired God's kingdom and righteousness, but according to God's word, he who pursues these things should be content to leave everything else in their Father's hands, and I have come woefully short in this area. God does not have the ability to lie, therefore, anything that He promises, because of His very nature He will deliver. God promised, "...[they] shall be added unto him." Earthly things will be added to us if we search after heavenly things first, even if they are not requested by us.

In Matthew 19:27, our Lord Jesus responds to Peter's query, "What shall we have then?" Is the same response given now to those who could ask the same question? He answers, "Verily I say unto you, 'There is no man that hath left house, or brethren, or sisters, or father, or mother, or wife, or children, or lands, for my sake, or the gospel's, but he shall receive a hundredfold now in this time, houses, and brethren, and sisters, and mothers, and children, and lands, with persecutions; and in the world to come eternal life'" (Mark 10:30).

I think it is reasonable to say that we cannot do many things well, much less perfectly yield to God. Only the Lord Jesus can make a completely unqualified, nothing-held-back-from-God guarantee since He was flawless, and we are fallible human beings.

Nonetheless, I believe the apostle Paul may provide us with some guidance on how to accomplish this. In 1 Corinthians 6:19, he asks a very profound inquiry, "What? Know ye not that your body is the temple of the Holy Ghost, which is in you, which ye have of God, and ye are not your own?"

We must fully realize that from the moment we accepted Jesus Christ into our hearts, He demanded complete self-surrender to His Holy Spirit. That surrender necessitates every minute area must be given over to him.

Many soldiers in God's army have faked their surrender. But when Jesus stated, in John 6:38, "For I came down from heaven, not to do my own will, but the will of him that sent me," the sacrifice He made on the cross proved to the Father and to the world that He was showing us what genuine surrender should look like.

We must yield to the Holy Spirit, who will guide us in what we must do and whatever task the Father intends to accomplish through us. That is why the Apostle Paul implores us to bring our bodies before God. In Romans 12:1, he says the following, "I beseech you therefore, brethren, by the mercies of God, that ye present your bodies a living sacrifice, holy, acceptable unto God, which is your reasonable service."

He could not make this request of those who are not God's children, those who have not received Jesus Christ, but only of "brethren," those who have been converted and born again. This is not a work that can be done by the unrepentant but by those who have tasted God's mercies. Paul uses Old Testament imagery of an animal being sacrificed to God as a metaphor for what God expects from the "brethren." The animal had no self-will, so it could not offer its tail or a limb once it was killed; it was completely surrendered as a sacrifice.

What a beautiful picture the apostle has given us of what a life surrendered should look like! The sacrifice had to be perfect in every manner, as well as all that was given to God. It implies that I have a responsibility to ask God to take away any aspects of His disapproval from my life that the Holy Spirit makes me aware of but of which I was previously ignorant.

I can honestly state that, although I was attentive and caring about my health, I was not as intentional in its care before I was struck by the **"Silent Killer"** as I am now. We are for the most part a reactive group of people. We often wait until something happens then we try corrective measures, but sometimes that's too late! It is my responsibility to seek the Holy Spirit's guidance on how to take care of His temple now that the Holy Spirit has made me seriously aware of the importance and need to do so.

"Who has legal rights over one's body and how it is to be cared for?" is a multibillion-dollar question that demands an immediate solution from everyone. The answer to this question is determined by the person to whom the inquiry is addressed. Non-Christians will almost always respond by saying they have exclusive rights to their bodies.

But when someone who has been born again and knows the Bible is asked about it, they will immediately respond that their body, this incredible organism, is the lawful property of their Creator God. Before being struck by the **"Silent Killer,"** I knew instinctively or biblically that the instant I surrendered my life to Jesus Christ, I was relinquishing my ultimate rights to His Holy Spirit. That is not to say I have always let Him have complete reign over my life.

My religious mind would tell me that God is in "complete charge" most of the time, but my natural behavior would contradict my religious mind. For example, I was aware that my body, according to the Bible, is the Lord's temple. I learned that a temple is a sacred structure, or a location dedicated to the service or worship of God or gods. Academically, I knew that a setting like this deserved to be treated with respect, care, and understanding. Despite this, my actions frequently contradicted my knowledge.

Knowledge can only be useful if it is accompanied by wisdom. God welcomes those seeking wisdom to come to Him and ask for it, and He promises to lavishly give it to them. "If any of you lack wisdom, let him ask of God, that giveth to all men liberally, and upbraideth not; and it shall be given him" (James 1:5).

Struck By The Silent Killer

One of my most common petitions was for wisdom. There were occasions, however, when I was confronted with a scenario and did not know what to do. Despite the fact that I was aware that God had given me the opportunity to ask for wisdom and had promised to happily offer it to those who asked so that they may make the best decisions possible, I did not do so frequently when it came to my health.

God does not offer or grant wisdom to everyone; rather, only those who recognize their lack and ask for it will get it. There are those who believe they have everything figured out; they are arrogant in their belief that they know everything and are full of wisdom.

Even God's people, truth be told, often lack His insight on how to deal with life's daily challenges, how to improve our health, love one another, and effectively combat the devil. Of course, we can ask for wisdom in a casual manner, but if it is not done on purpose, the answer may not come.

So, in legal words, who owns your body? In terms of creation, God owns your body, but your body has legal rights in the hands of the person you have given it to. Many years ago, on a Friday night, at the New Testament Church of God on Willesden High Road in London, I repented of my sins and requested Jesus to come into my life. I gladly abandoned all legal rights to my life from that point forward; from that time forward, Jesus has owned me, and I am His slave.

Many people, especially in today's politically correct world, may find this a source of controversy and conflict. But the Apostle Paul asked the question, "Know ye not, that to whom ye yield yourselves servants to obey, his servants ye are to whom ye obey; whether of sin unto death, or of obedience unto righteousness?" says the Bible, the word of God (Romans 6:16).

Every person is a servant of the monarch to whom he or she is subjected. Because of their ignorance, many individuals are unaware that they are willing servants of Satan. This is not a new occurrence. There is a wonderful story that demonstrates how even the most religious people can overlook this fact.

Victory Over Stroke

In John's gospel, chapter 8, we find Jesus Christ in a heated dispute with a group of religious people who believed God was their Father. Imagine their amazement when Jesus told them that Satan, not God, was their spiritual father. These religious individuals were unaware that they were agents of Satan.

Jesus was a hard worker; the day before, He had been teaching, and the next morning He got up early to do it all over again. "My meat is to do the will of him that sent me, and to finish his work," Jesus reportedly told his disciples in John 4:34.

Many would urge Him today, "Take it easy, Jesus. Use wisdom and look after yourself. Take the day off, go fishing or anything." Nobody knew what He had for dinner or where He had spent the night. He did not make a public appearance during the night, possibly because assassins were pursuing Him. Without abandoning His royal duties, He went about performing His duty for which He had traveled to Earth, well aware that His time to die was approaching.

Jesus was unaffected by the task or the people in any way. Never did He ask, "Do I have to do it all over again?" He took pleasure in carrying out the mission for which He was sent. Yet, there was one moment when He begged, "O my Father, if it be possible, let this cup pass from me: nevertheless, not as I will, but as thou wilt," (Matthew 26:39). This prayer demonstrated Jesus' humanity.

Jesus suffered the majority of His unfavorable confrontations from individuals claiming to be God's messengers, despite the fact that He served faultless. Regardless, He never allowed anxiety or stress into His life. I have been in a lot of circumstances that, in retrospect, may have caused me a lot of stress but that I did not identify or classify it as such, either due to ignorance or a refusal to admit it.

They knew where He was, and those who wanted to hear Him arrived early at the temple. His audience was diverse, with no one there for the same purpose. For some, His words were a double-edged blade, but for others, they were medicine and food, just what they needed to mend their broken hearts and feed their starving souls.

Struck By The Silent Killer

Gospel preachers can be naïve to expect that everyone who comes to hear them will love and appreciate them, or that everyone will come for the same reason. Jesus was not befuddled by any of the people who were present. While Jesus was speaking, the scribes and Pharisees arrived, but not to learn from Him. They stopped Him and anyone else who was listening in order to foment a feud with Him and lure Him into a trap.

At the time of Jesus' preaching, the scribes and Pharisees were two basically independent and opposing factions. They were both well-known lawyers. Scribes were legal specialists capable of drafting legal documents (contracts for marriage, divorce, loans, inheritance, mortgages, the sale of land, and the like). In every community, there was at least one writer. Pharisees belonged to a religious sect that believed in the afterlife and followed legal norms related to "the fathers' traditions," rather than the Bible.

God's temple was changed into a courthouse by these two legal groups and Jesus was unofficially appointed as their unelected judge, since they did not like Him. They were certain that they had found themselves in a doctrinal quagmire. "Master, this woman was taken in adultery, in the very act..." they explained as they handed him a detainee (John 8:4). Despite their claims, she was captured and brought to Him alone, as if she committed the act all by herself.

The scribes and Pharisees brought this lady to Christ and placed her in the midst of the gathering, intending for her to be judged solely by Christ. Everyone knew that adultery was punished by death under Jewish law, which the Roman authority allowed, so she was brought before the holy court.

Even the most devout religious people can unwittingly surrender their bodies to Satan. The scribes and Pharisees who brought this adulterous woman to Jesus were scripturally correct. However, in bringing this case before the court of heaven, the scribes and Pharisees showed their bias. "And the man that committeth adultery with another man's wife, even he that committeth adultery with his neighbour's wife, the adulterer and the adulteress shall surely be put to death" (Leviticus 20:10).

"If a man be found lying with a woman married to a husband, then they shall both of them die, both the man that lay with the woman, and the woman: so shalt thou put away evil from Israel" (Deuteronomy 22:22). It was impossible for the woman to commit adultery by herself. Entrapment of Jesus was their sole purpose. Because they were agents of Satan and by their rejection of Jesus, they surrendered themselves solely unto the wicked one.

If you are not born again, you are completely under Satan's control, and you may be completely unaware of it. The only time he cannot claim ownership of you is when you repent of your sins and ask Jesus to come into your heart.

God owns those who are born again twice: once when He created them and again when He redeemed them from their sins. Unbelievers have no choice; they cannot straddle the fence or serve two masters. Christian servitude to God is voluntary and comes from a free will, but unbelievers have no choice.

God wants us to think of our bodies as thankful stewards rather than self-governing entities. Until it returns to the ground from where it was taken, the body will always belong to God. It was created by Him for His own amusement. After grasping that all bodies belong to God, the next level is to willingly give this lump of dirt up to Him completely for His divine purposes.

According to Revelation 4:11, Almighty God created the body for the sake of pleasure, His own pleasure. "Thou art worthy, O Lord, to receive glory and honour and power: for thou hast created all things, and **for thy pleasure** they are and were created." Not only did God create "all things," but we were also taught the reason for their creation, to give God pleasure.

If something gives you pleasure, you get a feeling of happiness, satisfaction, or enjoyment from it. But is your life bringing satisfaction to God? God created this amazing organism called the body and it is His property. He wants us to take good care of it and use it for His good pleasure.

Struck By The Silent Killer

Who has authority over you? Who has authority over your body, your emotions, your thoughts and actions, and over the consequences of your actions? The answer is up to you and you alone. Sometimes we behave in ways to seek validation and approval from others such as our spouse, parents, teachers or even pastors. We need validation or approval only from God, no one else. God loves us and has created us for a special purpose. I know this to be a fact because God says so and He cannot lie.

In Ephesians, He says you are God's masterpiece. You were created for good works by Him before you were even born. He wants us to live our lives fulfilling what He wants through the gifts and talents He has given us. "For we are his workmanship, created in Christ Jesus unto good works, which God hath before ordained that we should walk in them" (Ephesians 2:10).

CHAPTER 11
Stress and Stroke

F ew people would consider pastoral ministry to be a "high-stress" job. After all, pastors like myself encourage people to cast their worries on the Lord, because He is concerned about them.

This is completely biblical. "Casting all your cares upon him; for he careth for you" (1 Peter 5:8). The admonition is to "throw all" on Jesus. Stress is "a feeling of physical or mental tension," according to the Medical Encyclopedia ("Stress and Your Health"). However, stress is referred to in the Bible as "cares." When we examine stress from this biblical perspective, we can learn how to deal with it.

According to Genesis 3, God cursed the land from which Adam was taken and over which Adam was to have dominion because of Adam's willful disobedience (Genesis 3:17). As long as we are alive, we will encounter events that give us concern or emotional strain, and how we respond to them is what matters most. It is our non-biblical reactions to mental and emotional tension that causes stress.

The Apostle Paul in writing to the Philippians brethren gave them insight as to how to deal with any potential stressful or emotional strain. He told them "Be careful for nothing; but in every thing by prayer and supplication with thanksgiving let your requests be made known unto God" (Philippians 4:6).

If a friend knows that misfortune and impending doom is near and says to you "Don't worry, my friend. It's going to be okay." That suggestion may result in a great deal more anxiety and you might respond, "Why should I not worry?"

Some would ask, "How can a person who is faced with actual issues not be nervous about them?" Is Paul arguing that one should pretend that things are not real when he says "Be careful for nothing"? Does this imply that we are to be unconcerned about worldly problems, or that we should do nothing if our home is in danger of foreclosure?

A proper interpretation of the Bible would show that this is not what Paul is stating. I believe he is saying is that there is a level of faith in God that allows one to remain free of fear and at peace even in the face of looming unpleasant situations.

Not only does he advise the listeners not to be nervous or "careful for naught," but he also utilizes the conjunction "but" to convey his three stress-relieving steps: prayer, supplication, and thanksgiving. "But in everything by prayer and supplication with thanksgiving let your requests be made known unto God" (Philippians 4:6).

I have been in circumstances where I have felt like I was up against the proverbial wall, and I have prayed, but not always with the desired outcomes. I would let the devil make all kinds of proposals to me, and I would often follow his diabolical advice because I was ignorant. What Paul is stating is that if his methods are followed, the situations that might have otherwise generate stress and may lead to a stroke will be alleviated.

The term or phrase "in everything" is the first thing to notice in his advice. It means that if anything is important enough to cause me stress, I should take it to God. Obviously, we do not pray for everything because not everything is worrisome. As a result, I must first accept the alarming situation. Although it is possible to generalize, this issue necessitates self-awareness, honesty, and humility. Yes, I confessed my inner cares to God, but it was not always easy for me to admit to myself or someone else that I was drowning in my inner cares.

Struck By The Silent Killer

"In every situation." If something is big enough to make me stress, it is big enough for me to talk to God about. If, on the other hand, I am not in good standing with Him, I will not be able to go to Hm in faith unless I first repent of any sin-related barriers. "If I regard iniquity in my heart, the Lord will not hear me" (Psalms 66:18).

If a person does not pray about everything, he will be stressed about most things. To be honest, I did not pray about all of my problems. Some things did not seem "serious enough" to bring to God in prayer. I was actually giving stress permission to ruin my life since I did not pray about everything. I am learning that there are options; I have to choose whether to follow Paul's advice for a positive outcome or to continue doing things my way and end up with a stressful ending.

'By prayer and supplication,' says the author. Many people's sole concept of prayer is asking God to provide them with something they desire, even though their hearts are empty of God and filled with the cares of the world. By what foundation or with what confidence can one ask of Him, if there is no closeness, contact, or fellowship with him? "And this is the confidence that we have in him, that, if we ask any thing according to his will, he heareth us" (1 John 5:14). When I am certain of my relationship with the Father and go to him, prayer will become a relational experience rather than a religious one. I believe many who are "church goers" are at a religious stage rather than the experiential stage.

As gospel preachers, we have an intrinsic ability to declare and teach even what we have never experienced. It is like teaching about spiritual gifts, although we may not be sure what they are. In contrast, the Apostle Paul wrote mostly from personal experience. When for example he tells us not to be "ignorant" of spiritual gifts, it is because he was able to identify all the gifts.

Was it conceivable for Paul to feel "stressed out" in any way? Had stress ever knocked on his heart's door, saying, "I am here; let me in"? Imagine being lied about, insulted, beaten unjustly and severely, and thrown into the Philippians' highest security jail without a proper hearing. How might you have handled that scenario? I might have been stressed out of my mind.

Victory Over Stroke

In Acts 16:22-25, we read

> "And the multitude rose up together against them: and the magistrates rent off their clothes, and commanded to beat them. And when they had laid many stripes upon them, they cast them into prison, charging the jailor to keep them safely: who, having received such a charge, thrust them into the inner prison, and made their feet fast in the stocks. And at midnight Paul and Silas prayed, and sang praises unto God: and the prisoners heard them. Was it a particularly tense period for them? Should they have pretended that the situation they were in was capable of driving them bonkers?

How did they deal with a potential stressful situation? Their solution was to pray and sing songs to God. In other words, they worshipped God. This is exactly what Job did after he got news that his entire possessions, including his ten children, were all destroyed.

The result is absolutely remarkable. Not only were they released supernaturally, but when the jailor was rescued from suicidal ideation, he asked "Sirs, what must I do to be saved?" (Acts16:30). The answer? "And they said, 'Believe on the Lord Jesus Christ, and thou shalt be saved, and thy house'" (Acts 16:31). Not only did their stress-free handling of the situation lead to their supernatural release, but it also led to the salvation of their jailor and his family.

"Thou wilt keep him in perfect peace, whose mind is stayed on thee: because he trusteth in thee," the prophet stated in Isaiah 26:3, and Paul must have heard him. So, stress does not have to have power over the believer; the believer should be in charge at all times, regardless of the circumstances. This, however, has to be learnt and practiced. It will not occur by happenstance.

The mindset that God is teaching us to cultivate is the polar opposite of stress. Stress-free living begins with faith in God. Even when you are under strain, just follow this advice. "Be careful for nothing; but in everything by prayer and supplication with thanksgiving let your requests be made known unto God" (Philippians 4:6).

Struck By The Silent Killer

God's original design for humanity was for us to live a "stress-free life" rather than a "stress- filled life." As a result of Adam's sin, man's existence on the planet will always be difficult and stressful. "Cursed is the ground for thy sake; in sorrow shalt thou eat of it all the days of thy life," God said to Adam in Genesis 3:17.

God designed life's adversity to bring humans back to a place of total reliance on Him. If we accept this, then our primary goal in any scenario should be to discover how to satisfy Him in that situation rather than simply looking for a way out.

It will not be difficult for us to give thanks "in everything," if we have reached that level of maturity. Because we will know that "this is the will of God in Christ Jesus concerning you" as stated in 1 Thessalonians 5:18. Unbelievers will be astounded by God's peace in the believer's life, and because it may be beyond their comprehension, they may inquire as to how they, too, can have this peace, as in the instance of Paul and the Philippian jailor. Is it true that "everyone suffers from stress at some point in their lives"? And if so, how did the Lord Jesus and the Apostle Paul deal with their stress? "For we have not an high priest which cannot be touched with the feeling of our infirmities; but was in all points tempted like as we are, yet without sin" (Hebrews 4:15).

Let us make a concerted effort to remember and act on this, "Cast thy burden upon the LORD, and he shall sustain thee: he shall never suffer the righteous to be moved" (Psalms 55:22).

CHAPTER 12
Physical Therapy Benefits

E very morning, I determined that I was going to beat this, that I was going to perform kingdom work, and that my stroke would be a part of my testimony to God's majesty.

When I was released from the hospital, I wrestled with the question of when I would get better. I decided to fast for three days in order to hear from God about whether I should seek divine healing or seek treatment, namely physical therapy. After the fast, I felt led by the Lord to go to physical therapy, so I did so for about six weeks. Throughout the process, the Lord provided me with the chance to acquire some really valuable lessons.

One of the things the Holy Spirit revealed to me was that I was not disciplined enough to take care of my body without going through therapy and putting in the labor and effort required to restore my body to its previous state. Not only that, but I believe that if I had received supernatural intervention, I would not have been as disciplined about caring for my health as I am now.

I have learned and continue to learn from the process that scripture is absolutely right when it says, "…with God, all things are possible" (Matthew 19:26). I made a conscious decision to use this experience for God's honor and glory, and I am continuing to do so. I want everyone who hears to know that all things work together for good to those who love God (Romans 8:28).

Victory Over Stroke

There was never a time during this ordeal when I felt scared, petrified, or alone because I was always calm and assured that the Holy Spirit was with me, and it is truly amazing how calm I felt. Of course, my thoughts would wander, and different scenarios would come to mind, but I quickly countered them with the word of God.

It is truly incredible how the word of God can and does appear at the time when it is most needed.

CHAPTER 13
Benefits of Sickness

Most of us have been sick at some point in our lives, and even if you have not, there is always the risk that you will. Sickness, according to the Lord Jesus Christ, is a curse, a product of the fall, and a devilish activity.

It is reported that wherever the Lord Jesus Christ went, wherever there was a need for healing, He healed the ill of whatever ailment they were suffering from. If it was not His will for individuals to be healed, He would have shown them the benefits of being sick and ways in which to endure the sickness as a part of His father's plan for their lives.

Instead, Jesus healed the lame, blind, lepers, deaf, dumb and those who were paralyzed. He rebuked fevers, straightened backs, casted out demons and, of course, raised the dead. "How God anointed Jesus of Nazareth with the Holy Ghost and with power: who went about doing good, and healing all that were oppressed of the devil; for God was with him" (Acts 10:38).

I am not aware of anyone who believes that ailments, diseases, and suffering are necessary and beneficial in any way. Those who "are destroyed" due to a lack of knowledge, often see afflictions as evil. However, the Bible is awash with examples whereby positive benefits are derived from sickness. In specific, the psalmist wrote about the benefits of suffering. He says that the discipline of the Lord, through sickness, can cause us to change our habits and thus learn godly lessons. In Psalms 119:71, he stated, "It is good for me that I have been afflicted, that I might learn your statutes."

Struck By The Silent Killer

Regardless of how we have treated our compassionate father, He has lavished us with far more than we deserve, all because of His goodness. We should pray and beg Him to teach us the lessons he wants us to learn from our current situation, rather than grumbling.

Satan can be the source of illness.
Several times in the Bible, Satan is singled out as solely responsible for certain sicknesses. According to Luke's account, Jesus healed a woman who had been plagued by a spirit of infirmity for eighteen years. Following her healing, the Lord informed the hypocrites that she was a daughter of Abraham who had been enslaved by Satan.

We read in Luke 13:16, "And ought not this woman, being a daughter of Abraham, whom Satan hath bound for lo, these eighteen years, to be loosed from this bond on the sabbath day?" So, her crippled condition was because of Satan's grip on her body.

I immediately blamed Satan for my position when I was struck by the "Silent Killer." I assumed he was acting in retaliation for the healings God had performed the day before. But people are sick for a multitude of reasons, all of which stem from Satan's deception in the Garden of Eden. As a result, sin is the bedrock of all disease. It is very obvious in the Bible. There was no sickness or death before sin. Adam's sin resulted in sin, disease, and death. Many of these maladies, on the other hand, can be avoided by adhering to God's dietary commandments. And even though I was not sick or unwell, I was aware that if I did not maximize my care, I might get ill.

One of the Bible's narratives is a story about Job and God. God had recently boasted about how perfect his servant Job was, and as a response, He gave Satan limited power over Job's body and all of Job's possessions. God granted His consent in Job 1:12, when He stated, "...all that he hath is thy power...," thus, everything that happened to Job was in God's perfect will. Satan has no power against man till God gives it. Although Satan asks God to "...put forth thine hand now...," God would not touch Job with His own hand. But He allowed the enemy to do so.

Job's afflictions stemmed from the malice of Satan, but the Lord's permission of this was for wise and holy purposes.

Victory Over Stroke

There is an evil spirit, the enemy of God and of all righteousness, who is continually seeking to distress, to lead astray, and, if possible, to destroy those who love God. How far his influence may extend, we cannot say; but probably much unsteadiness and unhappiness in Christians may be ascribed to him. While we are on this earth we are within his reach. Hence it behooves us to be sober and vigilant. "Be sober, be vigilant; because your adversary the devil, as a roaring lion, walketh about, seeking whom he may devour." (1 Peter 5:8).

God's people are taken under His special protection, they, and all that belong to them. The blessing of the Lord makes rich; Satan himself knows it. God permitted Job to be tried, as he suffered Peter to be sifted like wheat. It is our comfort to know that God has the devil on a chain. He has no power to lead men to sin but what they give him themselves; nor does he have any power to afflict men but what is given him by God.

If I did not have firsthand experience of our supernatural God's awesomeness, I would be astounded that a loving and compassionate God would allow such atrocities to afflict an adversary, let alone a guy he declared to be perfect and upright. This type of love baffles the natural man's understanding. No wonder we are informed that the natural man, or someone who has not been born again, cannot fully comprehend God's secrets. It does not mean he cannot; it just means he can only accomplish it if he has the Holy Spirit living within him.

CHAPTER 14
My Recovery

I did not start physical therapy until three months after being struck by the "Silent Killer." I am not sure if that was the best decision. According to experts, the sooner you enter rehabilitation, the better your chances of recovery.

I was determined to do everything I could with the Holy Spirit's guidance in order to achieve complete healing. "I can do all things through Christ who strengtheneth me," Paul said in Philippians 4:13, and he meant it. That struck a chord with me, and I did not think it was a cliché.

Before the stroke, I thought divine healing entailed accepting God's word, believing that healing is paid for by Jesus Christ's blood, praying with faith, and waiting patiently for the desired result. I still believe those things, but unless you are the one living through it, it is all theory to you.

The ongoing mental battle has been the most challenging component of my recuperation. Most of the time, no one is there to encourage you to keep fighting. There could be a variety of causes for this, including a lack of words, which is not always a bad thing.

Some people are not as subtle with their comments to the sick, and instead of offering words of comfort and faith, their words poison the soul. Again, we look back at the story of Job. When word went out that he was seriously ill, three of his buddies showed up. After what they said to Job, it would have been better for him if they had not showed up at all.

Struck By The Silent Killer

Job's third chapter opens with a fantastic lesson. They planned to visit him and console him, but they never did. Setting aside time from their schedule was a noble thing to do, and their motivation was excellent as well, but they lacked wisdom, which appears to imply that even with the best of intentions, you can cause more harm than good.

These three pals were not altogether detrimental; they performed at least three positive things. First, they came when they heard he was in pain, and secondly, they showed genuine concern. "And when they lifted up their eyes afar off, and knew him not, they lifted up their voice and wept; and they rent every one his mantle, and sprinkled dust upon their heads toward heaven" (Job 2:12). And according to verse 13, they stayed with him for seven days before saying a word or offering advice, and even in their silence, they were all on the same page.

However, their silence did not last long, and we have their utterances from chapters 4 to 25 recorded verbatim, including many lies, such as why God allows people to suffer. When they got to the conclusion that Job's suffering was due to whatever he had done wrong, they were playing the all-knowing game. They repeatedly urged him to confess and repent of his sins in order for God to bless him once more.

I cannot say that my friends have acted exactly like Job's friends, but I do get comments that imply the **"Silent Killer"** struck me was because of something I did wrong, and they may be correct. But the way it is said makes them appear as if they have it all together and have never gotten sick, or that they will never get sick because they are so on point.

Much can be gained from the story of Job and his friends. For example, as a word of caution to the wise, if you do not know what is going on in someone's life directly when they are recovering or sick, the best thing you can do is pray for them. Job's companions did not do this; instead, they ranted and raved, resulting in God's wrath. Job had no choice but to pray for them in the end. It is fortunate that he had the ability to pray effectively.

There is much that can be gleaned from the story, both good and terrible. When we become aware of a friend who is suffering, we might follow in these friends' footsteps by going to see him, mourning with him if required, and spending quality time with him.

Those are some notable examples. Even if we don't say much or nothing at all, I believe our physical presence with a hurting buddy can be a big comfort.

The blunders of Job's friends also contain a treasure of knowledge. Job's tragedies, they believed, were proof of God's wrath. In fact, the first to speak posed two profoundly religious questions: "Remember, I pray thee, who ever perished, being innocent? or where the righteous cut off?" (Job 4:7). You or the person who is suffering may never understand why they are suffering; Job had no idea that God was delighted with him and was bragging about him to Satan. Is it feasible that God is extolling the virtues of the sick person? Because you may never know, your obligation is to obey God's word, as stated in Romans 12:15, "Rejoice with them that do rejoice, and weep with them that weep."

My recovery began in the hospital as soon as I was given the diagnosis and assigned to a ward bed. I was convinced that the God I had been serving would deliver me from this mountain of a problem. There have been and will continue to be times when my mind is viciously assailed by the same repeating questions, "Will I ever return to my pre-stroke state of being? If so, when?"

Remembering God's promises is the only thing that gets me through those moments. One of these is mentioned in 1 John 5:14. "And this is the confidence that we have in him, that, if we ask any thing according to his will, he heareth us: And if we know that he hears us, whatsoever we ask, we know that we have the petitions that we desired of him" (1 John 5:15).

Confidence is crucial; it is trust and faith. On a daily basis, we all exercise some level of faith. But we are occasionally disillusioned because the person or thing in whom we placed our complete trust failed us. God, on the other hand, is unique in that He cannot fail.

The confidence referred to here is that which relates to the answer to prayer. God has the ability and power to bring whatever He promises to pass. He has made provision for spiritual and bodily healing for each of us via Jesus Christ, who took all of our illnesses and ailments, including stroke, to the cross where He was crucified at Calvary.

Struck By The Silent Killer

God not only listens to our prayers, but He also promises to answer them if they are in accordance with His will. He will not grant anything that is contradictory to His will or to what He has said. If someone asks for forgiveness of sins, He will forgive them; if they are in need for any reason and turn to God in faith for assistance, He will provide it.

The Bible is the only source of information about God's will for one's life. Although man has a natural predisposition to make promises and then break them, God will never break a promise He has given to man. Sometimes we truly intend to keep our commitments, but unforeseen circumstances happen, or we lack the ability to do so in the first place, but God keeps all of His promises. We can trust Him.

CHAPTER 15

The Importance of Self-Discipline

It has been estimated that there are over 4,000 religions in the world, however, when referring to religious groups, the six most recognized are Christianity, Judaism, Muslim, Islam, Buddhism, and Hinduism (Smith). What distinguishes each adhering group from the others? Most, if not all, would acknowledge and even attest to the fact that we are all created by the same All-Powerful God. However, it cannot be denied that Christianity has several distinctive features that set it apart from all other religions.

One of the largest contrasts is that the majority of Christians do not believe in doing enough in good deeds to gain God's favor and get entrance into His heaven. According to Paul, "For by grace are ye saved through faith; and that not of yourselves: it is the gift of God" (Ephesians 2:8). Christians firmly believe that no one can enter heaven through their own efforts, but only through God's gift of His son Jesus Christ. Jesus says, "I am the way, the truth, and the life: no man cometh to the Father, but by me" (John 14:6). Unfortunately, many people who believe in heaven do not agree with this assertion.

But because of the enormous demands that Christianity places on its adherents, many people struggle with it. For instance, Christians are expected to lead disciplined lives. Because many people do not understand the scriptures, when they read certain demands, they immediately decide that they are unable to fulfill those demands. This is because they are unaware that, upon accepting Jesus Christ into their lives, the Holy Spirit, the third member of the God family, immediately moves into that person's heart.

It is for this reason, among others, that the Apostle Paul penned these words, "What? know ye not that your body is the temple of the Holy Ghost which is in you, which ye have of God, and ye are not your own?" (1 Corinthians 6:19). Many people have been unable to fully comprehend what is expected of them by God due to their ignorance. The role of this person, known as the Holy Ghost, is to instruct those desiring to obey God in what they ought to do. However, He will not go against a person's wishes, and He will not offer assistance where God has not made it clear in the Bible, or when it is against God's will.

Self-discipline may be the most crucial aspect of required compliance to the word of God. It is listed as "temperance" among the fruit of the spirit by the Apostle Paul in Galatians 5:22–23 and is sometimes referred to as self-control as well. But what is self-discipline? In general, the Greek word translated "discipline" (enkrateia) comes from the root krat, which denotes power or lordship. Self-discipline means to exercise power over one's self, or keep oneself under control. The word indicates self-mastery over one's inner desires, thoughts, actions, and words.

Although the term self-discipline or self-control is not used in the Bible, self-discipline is clearly a crucial attribute of the Christian life. When for instance Jesus called his disciples to follow Him, He was really calling them into a disciplined lifestyle. They upon agreeing on His terms had to be willing to relinquish their feelings, impulses, desires for material and physical comforts; their flesh had to be under constant restraint.

Getting these new disciples out of their pre-Christian perspective was the first thing that needed to be done. This was required because they would need to practice self-control in the future, and that self-control would require a mental regeneration.

A person makes an exchange when he is convinced of his sin and decides to accept what Jesus accomplished for him. He decides to surrender by faith to His Lordship rather than continuing to do things his way. Self-denial implies that "I am ready to completely give up my life and my self- will for the good of the kingdom; I am ready to die to my own ways in the same way that Christ died in my place."

Struck By The Silent Killer

Similarly, many members of the body of Christ struggle to maintain a healthy dietary routine. They have tried to follow a specific diet, yet frequently find themselves straying from it. I do not claim to understand the causes, but I find it difficult to believe that food in and of itself could exert unchecked influence over a person's will.

I have first-hand knowledge of the effects of food. I was warned that after being hit by the "Silent Killer," I needed to be extremely cautious about what I ate. I was not addicted to any one thing, but there are a few items that I used to enjoy but now can only eat in very small portions.

My natural tendency is to encourage health rather than risk endangering the temple of God by ingesting anything that might not do so. I realize that I must practice self-control, follow the advice of the medical experts, and submit to the prodding of the Holy Spirit when it comes to my eating habits rather than relying solely on my own judgment.

Once more, self-control gives you the ability to decide what is best for God's sanctuary, your body. Is eating food a sin? Naturally, the response is a categorical no. However, gluttony, excessive consumption, and binge eating are sins. "For no man ever yet hated his own flesh; but nourisheth and cherisheth it...," according to Paul the Apostle (Ephesians 5:29).

However, although wanting the best for oneself is natural, does that always show in our behavior? Solomon said, ""He that hath no rule over his own spirit is like a city that is broken down, and without walls" (Proverbs 25:28). What lesson does this wise man wish to teach us, and why does he paint this picture utilizing the city, its walls, and a man's spirit? The person is a form of city, and self-control is a type of city wall. Solomon is comparing a person who lacks self-control and lack of discipline to an unprotected city. Perhaps he had lived in an era when cities were fortified with walls and guards to keep the populace safe. If the walls were pulled down, an attack could have been launched against them.

As a result, they would be powerless to fend off more assaults, and they would have definitely felt humiliated. The enemy would have full reign in the city. If the person's life is the wall, his body would be destroyed. The former citizen is now a prisoner. Because of no restraints placed on their appetites, many people are now captives of Satan.

Victory Over Stroke

Christians need to practice moderation in all areas of their lives, including their diets, emotions, moods, and actions. In other words, God desires for us to exercise firm control over all aspects of our lives, including our appetites. He does not desire for these things to possess such influence over us. "Does the world see a well-disciplined person in you, Errol Williams?" I ask myself. When Jesus stated, "Let your light so shine before men, that they may see your good works, and glorify your Father which is in heaven" (Matthew 5:16), was He referring to the fact that my life is an open book that is regularly read without my knowledge?

The need for discipline in the pew is as great as it is in the congregation. We see many leaders who seemingly are grossly overweight, at least so it would appear. Is that a good sign of "Do as I do"? Though I have no way of verifying what percentage of leaders are obese, I believe that number must be quite staggering.

Even to the inexperienced eyes, one thing is clear: the church is home to a growing obesity epidemic. Of course, this seriously jeopardizes the church's objective to spread the gospel throughout the world. I think it starts with self-discipline because it is apparent that unhealthy people will struggle more than healthy people.

You may ask, "What is the answer?" Some people might believe that the solution is to eliminate all foods, but that is obviously absurd. Instead, keep a close check on your meat intake, move away from processed meals, drink more water (this is an area where I find myself weak in self- control), eat more fruits and vegetables, and engage in your preferred kind of daily exercise. The body needs to be properly stewarded, which demands self-control and physical check-ups.

"But I keep under my body, and bring it into subjection: lest that by any means, when I have preached to others, I myself should be a castaway" (1 Corinthians 9:27).

God be praised.

Health Website References

"10 Ways to Control High Blood Pressure Without Medication." *Mayo Clinic,* 12 July 2022, *https://www.mayoclinic.org/diseases-conditions/high-blood-pressure/in-depth/high-blood- pressure/art-20046974.*

"12 Ways to Keep Your Brain Young." *Harvard Medical School, 13 May 2022, https://www. health.harvard.edu/mind-and-mood/12-ways-to-keep-your-brain-young.*

Björkhem, Ingemar, and Steve Meaney. "Brain Cholesterol: Long Secret Life Behind a Barrier." *Arteriosclerosis, Thrombosis, and Vascular Biology, vol. 24, 2004, pp.806–815. https:// doi.org/10.1161/01.ATV.0000120374.59826.1b.*

"Brain." *Cleveland Clinic, 30 Mar. 2022, https://my.clevelandclinic.org/ health/body/22638-brain. Brazier, Yvette. "How Does a CT or CAT Scan Work?" MedicalNewsToday, 24 July 2018, https://www.medicalnewstoday. com/articles/153201.*

"Carotid Artery Disease." *Mayo Clinic, 4 Oct. 2018, https://www.mayoc-linic.org/diseases- conditions /carotid-artery-disease/symptoms-causes/syc-20360519.*

"Causes of High Blood Pressure." *WebMD, 6 Aug. 2021, https://www.web-md.com /hypertension- high-blood-pressure/default.htm.*

"Cerebral Hypoxia." *Cleveland Clinic. 4 May 2021, https://my.clevelandclin-ic.org/health/diseases/6025cerebralhypoxia#:~:text=It%20needs%20oxy-gen%20to%20function,brain%20cells %20begin%20to%20die.*

Chudler, Eric H. "Nutrition and the Brain." *Neuroscience for Kids, 14 Sept. 2022, http://faculty. washington.edu/chudler/nutr.html.*

"Effects of Stroke." *John Hopkins Medicine. https://www.hopkinsmedicine. org/health/ conditions- and-diseases/stroke/effects-of-stroke.*

"Facts About Trans Fats." *MedlinePlus, 26 May 2020, https://medlineplus. gov/ency/patient instructions/000786.htm.*

"Getting Your Cholesterol Checked." *Centers for Disease Control and Prevention (CDC)*, 12 July 2022, https://www.cdc.gov/cholesterol/cholesterol_screening.htm.

Greenwald, Brian D. "Can the Brain Itself Feel Pain?" *Brainline*, 12 July 2012, https://www. brainline.org/author/brian-greenwald/qa/can-brain-itself-feel-pain.

"High Blood Pressure–Understanding the Silent Killer: The Who, What, Why, and How of High Blood Pressure." *U. S. Food and Drug Administration*. 21Jan. 2021, https://www.fda. gov/drugs/special-features/high-blood-pressure-understanding-silent-killer.

"High Cholesterol Facts." *Centers for Disease Control and Prevention (CDC)*, 12 July 2022. https://www.cdc.gov/cholesterol/facts.htm.

"How Many Neurons Are in the Brain?" *Brain Facts*, 4 Dec. 2018, https://www.brainfacts.org/in- the-lab /meet-the-researcher/2018/how-many-neurons-are-in-the-brain-120418.

"The Human Brain." *Rehabilitation Info Portal*, 30 Sept. 2022, http://www.rehabchicago.org/the- human-brain/.

"Hypertension." *World Health Organization*, 25 Aug. 2021, https://www.who.int/news-room/fact - sheets/detail/hypertension.

"Improving Fine Motor Skills." *American Stroke Association*, 4 Dec. 2018, https://www.stroke.org/en/about-stroke/effects-of-stroke/physical-effects-of-stroke/physical-impact/improving- fine-motor-skills.

Jaret, Peter. "High Blood Pressure." *WebMD*, 17 Sept. 2021, https://www.webmd.com/ hypertension-high-blood-pressure/guide/high-blood-pressure.

"Malnutrition." *John Hopkins Medicine*, https://www.hopkinsmedicine.org/health/conditions- and- diseases/malnutrition.

"Men and Stroke." *Centers for Disease Control and Prevention (CDC)*, 7 June 2022, https://www.cdc.gov/stroke/men.htm.

"More Women Die from Stroke Than Men." Memorial Care, https://www. memorialcare.org/blog/ more-women-die-stroke-men.

Morley, John E. "Undernutrition." Merck Manual, July 2021, https://www. merckmanuals.com /home/disorders-of-nutrition/undernutrition/undernutrition.

"Post-Stroke Challenges." Neofect, 14 Aug. 2019, https://www.neofect.com/ us/blog/post- stroke-challenges.

Raichle, Marcus E., and Debra A. Gusnard. "Appraising the Brain's Energy Budget." Proceedings of the National Academy of Sciences of the United States of America. vol. 99, no. 16, 2002, pp. 10237-10239. https://doi. org/10.1073/pnas.172399499.

Rao, Vani. "Neuropsychiatry of Stroke: Geriatric Workforce Enhancement Program." https://www.hopkinsmedicine.org/gec/series/neuropsych_stroke. html.

"Risk Factors for Stroke." John Hopkins Medicine. https://www.hopkinsmedicine.org/health/ conditions-and-diseases/stroke/risk-factors-for-stroke.

Scheidl, Nicole. "Water, Water, Water." Fit Minds, 2 July 2021, https://fit-minds.ca/brain-health- lifestyle- water-water-water/.

Smith, Sandra Hamer. "How Many Religions are There?" Christianity.com, 19 May 2022, https://www.christianity.com/wiki/cults-and-other-religions/ how-many-religions-are- there.html.

"Stress and Your Health." MedlinePlus, 30 April 2022, https://medlineplus. gov/ency/article 48 /003211.htm.

"Stroke: Emotional & Behavioral Changes." Cleveland Clinic, 8 June 2018, https://my.cleveland clinic.org/health/articles/13485-stroke-emotional--behavioral-changes.

"Stroke Statistics." Centers for Disease Control and Prevention (CDC), 15 April 2022, https://www.cdc.gov/stroke/ facts.htm#:~:text=2,Stroke%20statistics,disease%20was%20due%20to%20stroke.&text =Every%2040%20seconds%2C%20someone%20in,minutes%2C%20someone%20dies %20of%20 stroke.

"Stroke: Overview." John Hopkins Medicine. https://www.hopkinsmedicine. org/health/conditions -and-diseases/stroke.

Terry, John, and Bryan Ludwig. "What Happens During a Stroke?" Premier Health, 24 Jan. 2022, https://www.premierhealth.com/your-health/articles/ women-wisdom-wellness-/ what-happens-during-a-stroke-.

"Types of Stroke." WebMD, 23 Aug. 2022, https://www.webmd.com/stroke/ guide/types-stroke. "Understanding Blood Pressure Readings." American Heart Association. https://www.heart.org/en/health-topics/high-blood-pressure/understanding-blood-pressure-readings.

Wells, Diana. "Fun Facts About the Brain You Didn't Know." Healthline, 6 July 2017, https://www.healthline.com/health/fun-facts-about-the-brain.

"What is Cholesterol?" American Heart Association, 16 Nov. 2020, https:// www.heart.org/en /health-topics/cholesterol/about-cholesterol.

"What is High Blood Pressure?" American Heart Association, 31 Oct. 2016, https://www.heart.org/en/health-topics/high-blood-pressure/the-facts-about-high-blood-pressure/what-is- high-blood-pressure.

"What is Hypertension? A Mayo Clinic Expert Explains." Mayo Clinic, 15 Sept. 2022, https://www.mayoclinic.org/diseases-conditions/high-blood-pressure/multimedia/ vid-20538077#:~:text=Elevated%20blood%20pressure%20is%20defined,than%20or%2 0equal%20to%2080.

"What is a Stroke? A Mayo Clinic Expert Explains." Mayo Clinic, 20 Jan. 2022, https://www.mayoclinic.org/diseases-conditions/stroke/symptoms-causes/ syc-20350113#:~:text=There%20are%20two%20main%20causes,doesn't%20cause%20 lasting%20symptoms.

"What is Malnutrition?" Abbott, 23 Sept. 2021, https://www.nutritionnews. abbott/malnutrition /global-issue/what-is-malnutrition-/.

"Who Gets Vascular Dementia?" Alzheimer's Society, 21June 2022, https:// www.alzheimers. org.uk/about-dementia/types-dementia/risk-factors-vascular-dementia.

Lightning Source UK Ltd.
Milton Keynes UK
UKHW041046211222
414263UK00001B/119